The Encyclopedia of Modern American SMALL ARMS

The Encyclopedia of Modern American
SMALL ARMS

Clemens Elwell

Preface by Lt Col Arthur Alphin, US Army
Photo descriptions by Timothy Jacobs

Bison Books

First Published in 1987 by

Bison Books Ltd
176 Old Brompton Road
London SW5
England

ISBN 0 86124 370 6

Printed in Hong Kong

Acknowledgements

Many thanks to Pam Berkman and Ruth DeJauregui
for researching the photography in this book. Also, a
special thank you to Arthur Alphin for his help and
expertise without which this book would not have
been possible.

Photo Credits

All photos courtesy of the respective manufacturers
except:
Amon Carter Museum: 174-175
California State Library: 171
Canadian Pacific: 177 (bottom)
David Kramer Photography, via Weaver Arms Corp-
    oration: 114-115 (top)
Ian V Hogg: 191
Keystone Press Agency: 118-119 (bottom left)
Library of Congress: 163 (bottom), 178-179
Lowie Museum of Anthropology, University of Cali-
    fornia, Berkeley: 162
Mag-na-port: 46-47, 48-49, 60 (bottom left)
National Archives: 94-95
Paramount Pictures: 164-165
Robert Hunt Picture Library: 173
Sid Richardson Collection: 184-185
South Dakota State Historical Society: 183 (bottom)
Sutro Library: 6, 7, 8-9, 172
United States Department of Defense (including the
    United States Army and Air Force): 12-13, 53, 123
    (right), 124-125, 131, 152-153, 157 (top and bot-
    tom), 158 (top and bottom), 159, 167, 188-189, 192
United States Embassy, Beirut: 125 (inset)
© Bill Yenne: 11, 111, 127 (inset), 187

Designed by Ruth DeJauregui
Edited by Timothy Jacobs and John Kirk
Captioned by Timothy Jacobs

Page 1: The Chipmunk Silhouette Pistol, with
walnut stock; and *(in box)* Feather Industries'
AT-22, field stripped.

Pages 2-3: Top to bottom: The Ruger Mark II
Standard automatic pistol in stainless steel, the Remington Model 4 autoloading rifle with Monte Carlo
stock; and the Ruger 12 gauge over-and-under shotgun with a stainless steel receiver.

This page: The FIE Texas Ranger Revolver, with
special custom grips—the Texas Ranger is available
with standard hand-rubbed walnut grips.

CONTENTS

INTRODUCTION

A Unique Team:
The American Arms Industry
and the American Shooter

Throughout history the development of weaponry has always followed a closed loop cycle. Whether it was Ctesibus's work with the ballista (a type of catapult) before the birth of Christ, or the fielding of the M16A2 today, the pattern remains the same: A requirement is identified, a design is made, the design is tested, and after suitable modification it is manufactured and distributed. The cycle never ends—for as soon as one weapon is fielded, another need will be seen and the cycle will start again. This is true not only in military endeavors but in civilian shooting also: in the realm of target shooting for example, the search for the design breakthrough in accuracy never ends.

A good case can be made that in no place on earth—and at no time in the history of mankind—has this loop ever been more prolific than in the United States. Though many men of other nationalities (and at other times in history) have certainly designed weapons, nothing quite matches that which has occurred in the last three hundred years in this country. It has fostered what I believe is a unique team: the American arms industry and the American shooter, bonded together by a common goal and working for the betterment of all.

In America, identification of weapons requirements has traditionally come from a stunning array of sources. Those who identified requirements and commenced designing weapons were not necessarily those educated or trained to do so. More often than not users in the field would identify requirements and, in many cases, train themselves to make the next design.

Perhaps the classic example of this is the introduction of the .44 Magnum revolver. This revolver was specifically manufactured in response to requirements as identified by the late Elmer Keith. Mr Keith spent years in design experimentation as an interested shooter and as demand for his designs grew, the American firearms industry adopted his designs and produced the weapon. But Mr Keith has never been alone: In the area of weapons, America has always enjoyed the broadbased participation of both shooters and industry. In some cases (such as with Mr Keith) this has resulted in the manufacture of a certain design. In other cases, the result has demonstrated yet another strength.

If one participates at any point in the cycle—and has an understanding of the requirement and the particular design that satisfied that requirement—then one would also have an understanding of the strong points and weak points of the design, and how the weapon should be employed, so as to capitalize upon the strong points and defend against the weak points. Let us turn back to the founding of our nation to illustrate this point.

By the beginning of the eighteenth century, enough machinery had arrived in the New World to allow rudimentary arms manufacture to take place. This period saw the birth of what has come to be known as the Kentucky rifle. With few exceptions, firearms up to that time had been smoothbore;

Daniel Boone *(above)* relied heavily on his trusty 'Kentucky Rifle,' as did most early frontiersmen and settlers. The constant threat of Indian attack *(right)*, and the need to have a reliable means of bringing home meat for the winter led to the rapid sophistication of American small arms.

accuracy with such weapons was woefully poor compared to that of rifled weapons. Though the concept of rifling had been known for some time, a good means of employing rifling had not yet arrived. Since weapons had to be loaded from the muzzle, the projectile had to be smaller than the lands (high spots in a rifled bore) so that the projectile could be rammed home. But if the projectile was to be spun, it had to be larger than groove diameter (the low spots in the bore) so that the rifling in the bore could engrave corresponding marks on the projectile and induce spin as it traveled through the barrel. The Kentucky (or more properly Pennsylvania) rifle solved this problem by using a lubricated cloth or leather patch around the ball. This patch was engraved by the rifling when the weapon was loaded. Though such a system of patching the ball was a bit slow and awkward (and consequently not really suited for military purposes), the rifle was ideally suited for the con-

ditions of North America. The requirements of the settlers and colonists in North America fostered an arms industry which produced these rifles and, through subsequent iterations, constantly refined them with such techniques as false muzzles and gain twist in order to increase accuracy (and consequently range) or to improve reloading. This flurry of design, use and re-design simply did not occur anywhere else in the world. Further, it fostered a special breed of men such as Daniel Morgan.

At the battle of Cowpens during the American Revolution, the American commander, Morgan, was being pursued by a large number of British and Tories. Morgan's force was a mixed lot—both in weapons and in organization. Capitalizing upon his weapons, Morgan placed his riflemen in the front line, his militia armed with muskets in the middle line and his trained Continental infantry, also armed with muskets, in the rearmost line. As the British came on, his instructions to the riflemen were to kill any two selected targets and retreat along

a pre-determined path to the rear. The effect of this was that the riflemen could take their time in loading and aiming, and yet that they would not be forced to engage the enemy at close range—where the enemy's more rapidly reloaded smoothbore musket could overpower them by fire or where he could charge with the bayonet.

Morgan's plan worked perfectly. The British lost many casualties by simply advancing across the 200 yards of open ground in order to close with the Americans. Though they had suffered, the British had not yet had the opportunity to inflict any casualties upon the Americans. At the middle line, the Americans were hotly engaged and were pushed back by what in effect was a larger and more highly trained force. As the middle line gave way, the British were confronted with the American Continental Infantry who, if they had been engaged earlier, would have been outnumbered. At this point, however, the British ranks were depleted and weary. As the trained infantry of both sides locked in combat, the riflemen and militia (who had been reformed in the rear) closed upon one British flank while Morgan unleashed his cavalry upon the other. The result was the total destruction of the British force. Only a shooter who participated in the American closed loop system could so clearly analyze the situation and the relative strengths and weaknesses of his weapons.

At the time, the American arms industry was of course highly de-centralized. It consisted almost entirely of individual rifle-making shops. One might think that this de-centralization facilitated the participation of men like Daniel Morgan. However, the converse did not hold true. As America developed and its arms industry grew larger and more centralized, the system remained effective. The arms industry and the American shooter remained equal participants.

In the War Between the States, inventors and users alike identified weapons requirements and created the designs to fill the needs. Previously existing designs such as the Henry and the Sharps were rapidly refined. Others, like the Spencer, were created and fielded. These designs in turn brought about requirements in the areas of tool and cartridge case manufacture. In all cases, the goal was to either increase the volume of fire or increase the effective range. Though other countries had their own inventors, such as Boxer of England, nothing quite matched the American fervor. The demands of the War (and later, the demands of settling the American West) fostered intensive activity. Designs for primers, cartridge cases, bullets and rifles came from multitudes of different designers. Such names as Rodman, Farrington, Milbank, Berdan, Sharps, Spencer, Winchester and others surfaced again and again. It is significant that the Berdan primer is now standard throughout the world (except, strangely enough, in America where the requirement for reloading forces use of the Boxer primer), and that Berdan's impact extrusion method for the manufacture of cartridge cases has been the world's standard for over 100 years.

The demands of the American West and the demands of the eastern target ranges brought about a refinement of rifles and black powder cartridges equal to or better than anything else in the world. For example, the first Wimbledon Cup was not awarded for popping fuzzy little tennis balls over a net, but was awarded for rifle marksmanship; the first occupants of the plain at Wimbledon in England were target shooters. Their competitors were Americans from Creedmoor, Long Island. In

Left: American Indians often traded furs for rifles and muskets in the 18th century. Alliances with whites in their wars, and wars with the whites themselves brought gunpowder into the lives of many tribes.

matches at ranges up to 1000 yards the Americans took the cup. The ideas, experience and interest of the American hunters and target shooters were essential to the industry which in turn made the weapons that produced the margin of victory.

The appearance of smokeless powder in France in 1885 did not spell the doom of American weapons. The American refinement of weaponry was such that the black powder weapons still satisfied many of the requirements of North America. Further, the American cartridges and rifles were rapidly adapted to smokeless powder by the active and efficient American arms industry. This period, the 1880s and 1890s, showed a flurry of new development.

One of the guiding lights of this period was John Moses Browning. This incredibly prolific inventor designed one of the first strong and reliable lever action rifles that could handle the largest black powder cartridges of the day. Early in his career, Browning formed a partnership with Winchester. Winchester recognized the brilliance of Browning's designs, and bought the patents. Their part in the closed loop cycle was only to manufacture and market the weapons. Browning's single shot rifle of 1885 and his lever action rifle of 1886 put Winchester back in the forefront of arms manufacture. By 1892, Browning was creating lever action designs capable of handling smokeless powder. As the new century dawned, Browning designs encompassed military as well as sporting areas. The M1911 Colt pistol, for example, is just one of Browning's many designs.

The beginning of World War I saw the transfer to America of design and tooling for the manufacture of a turnbolt rifle—which borrowed some ideas from both the German Mauser and the American James Paris Lee. This rifle was the Pattern 14 Enfield (when manufactured in .303) and, upon American entry into the war, was manufactured (in .30-06) as the Pattern 17. After the war, the American shooter began to make his switch over from his preferred rifle of the pre-war years—the lever action—to the bolt action. The American arms industry stayed with the American shooter every step of the way. Even though the industry was now large and centralized, it still listened as the shooters identified requirements. For example, Remington kept the tooling which they had used to make Pattern 17s. In successive refinements they modified this to the Remington Model 30, Model 30S, Model 720, Model 721, Model 722, Model 725, and, finally, the Model 700 of today. At each step of the way they retained those features which were good and instituted improvements in order to satisfy the demand of the American shooter.

This bonding of the American arms industry and the American shooter in a drive to the common objective has never broken. A perusal of books or periodicals of the late 1950s and 1960s will clearly indicate the response of the American firearms industry—as new firearm models were fielded and as a blinding array of new cartridges and improved projectiles were manufactured in response to the requirements of the American hunter and the American target shooter. Earlier, I had identified the late Mr Elmer Keith. I also said that he was not alone. For example, the late Warren Page consolidated his testing results with the efforts of men such as Fred Huntington, Sr, and urged the American arms industry to field cartridges in 6mm. Remington took this data, and the data of their in-house designer, Mr Mike Walker and created the .244 Remington cartridge—now called the 6mm Remington. Winchester followed a similar path and created the .243 Winchester cartridge. These were clearly the result of the identification of requirements as shown by the American shooter.

Other names, of course, spring to mind. Bill Ruger of Sturm, Ruger & Company has been particularly adept in this area. He has kept a strong finger upon the pulse of the American shooter and properly identified the shooter's requirements. Capitalizing upon the experiments of others and his own considerable personal expertise, he has created a line of revolvers, rifles, shotguns and the company to make them. Lined up behind Ruger are such as Thompson Center with their Contender, and countless others. Such team work has only occurred in America.

While it is true that men of other nationalities have designed cartridges and weapons, a good case can be made that something unique has happened here in the United States. The breadth and speed of international weapons development has never exceeded the pace set here. Further—and perhaps more importantly—it is the depth and breadth of participation in the closed loop system that sets the United States apart from all others. The American firearms industry and the American shooter are both aware of that bond which exists as they forge ahead to the common goal. It works here like no place else. For example: if you have a field report on a Sierra bullet, simply write Mr Robert Hayden, the president of Sierra, and he will personally respond. No matter how busy he is, he's interested in what happens to his products and his desire to fill the requirements of the American shooter knows no bounds. It is significant that the American shooter freely and willingly participates in this team work. One might try writing to non-American outfits like RWS, but I caution that you won't get very far.

It is that link between the American firearms industry and the American shooter—that broad based participation in the closed loop cycle—which makes America, in the realm of firearms, separate from the rest of the world.

This book is a celebration of that bond. The multi-million dollar corporations and the one-man shops; they are all here. Though their means and resources may differ widely, they all function in the same way. They identify weapons requirements and produce designs to meet them. Whether it is Ruger or Remington, or the small one-man company, they do today that which Americans have done so well for the last 300 years: they identify a requirement, they design a solution, they test it and they manufacture it. This is their book.

Lt Col Arthur B Alphin is a firearms expert, instructor, and consultant. For the last two decades, he has been intimately involved with the design, testing, and use of all manner of military and civilian weapons and ammunition. A native of Virginia, Lt Col Alphin graduated from the US Military Academy in 1970 with a BS in Weapons Systems Engineering. Commissioned as a tanker, Lt Col Alphin served in tank units for eight years prior to earning an MA from Rice University. Subsequently, he taught at West Point where he established a course in Weapons Systems Technology. While an assistant professor at West Point, he guest lectured at colleges and universities throughout the United States. He also produced a series of instructional TV tapes on weaponry which have become part of the curriculum at USMA and throughout the ROTC system. Lt Col Alphin is currently the Director for Testing at Jefferson Proving Ground where he is responsible for the production acceptance testing of all Army conventional ammunition and the proof acceptance of gun tubes.

Parallel with his military career, Lt Col Alphin never dropped his private shooting activities. He shoots competitively and holds an NRA Master rating in pistol. His private experiments, which commenced in the early sixties, began to bear fruit in 1975. Applying his knowledge to the problem of large bore rifles, Lt Col Alphin made breakthroughs in rifle, cartridge and projectile design and, by 1979, established the A-Square Company, Inc. This company now supplies rifles and ammunition to trophy hunters and game departments throughout the world.

These marines (right) pose with legendary M-1 Garand service rifles—standard issue for US troops in World War II and Korea. This soldier (overleaf) holds a training version of today's Armed Forces standard issue: the Colt M-16.

PART I:
THE ENCYCLOPEDIA OF MODERN AMERICAN SMALL ARMS

PISTOLS

American Derringer Corporation

15 oz Derringers

Type: Single action with automatic barrel selection
Caliber: 24 calibers ranging from .22 long rifle to .44 Magnum
Barrel Length: 3"
Weight: 15 oz in .45 Auto Caliber
Finish: High polish or satin stainless steel
Capacity: 2 rounds

Designed as a short-range backup pistol, this derringer was ten years in the making. Built of stainless steel, the guns are finished with a high polish (looking like nickel plate) or a satin finish. All guns are equiped with a manually operated 'Hammer Block' type safety. The safety automatically disengages when the hammer is cocked.

The **Ultra Light Weight Derringer** is the same as the steel derringer except that high strength aircraft aluminum is used in place of some of the stainless steel parts. It is available in .38 Special or .38 S&W only. At 7.5 oz it is the lightest .38 Special caliber pistol ever made.

Model 3

Caliber: .38 Special
Barrel Length: 2.5"
Weight: 8.5 oz

The **Model 3** is a stainless steel, single shot derringer with the 'Hammer Lock' safety.

Model 4

Caliber: .45 Rifled barrel
Barrel Length: 4.1"
Weight: 16.5 oz
Finish: Satin or High Polish Stainless Steel
Capacity: 2 rounds

New for 1985, the **Model 4** has a manual 'Hammer Block' safety and will fire either .45 Colt, 2.5" .410 or 3" .410 shells. It is also available in .45 Auto, .45 Colt, .44 Special, .357 Magnum, and .357 Maximum. The Alaskan Survival Model has a .45–70 upper barrel and a 3" .410 or .45 Colt lower barrel.

Model 6

Caliber: .410 or .45 Colt
Barrel Length: 6"
Weight: 21 oz
Finish: Satin or High Polish Stainless Steel
Grips: Rosewood, Stag optional
Capacity: 2 rounds

The **Model 6** will fire .45 Colt and 2.5" or 3" .410 shells. Also featured on this model is the manual Hammer-Block safety.

Semmerling LM-4

Type: Double-action manual slide
Caliber: .45 ACP, 9mm
Overall Length: 5.2"
Weight: 24 oz
Finish: Semi-matte blue, Stainless steel
Capacity: 4 rounds

The unique pocket-sized pistol (5.2×3.7×1") is an entirely new design—smaller than any other .45 on the market today. The **LM-4** holds five rounds of .45 ACP ammunition, fed from a magazine by manual slide actuation (4 rounds in the magazine and one in the chamber.) As a double-action pistol, the LM-4 is extremely safe because the trigger bar prevents any forward motion of the striker unless the trigger is pulled all the way. In addition to this, the trigger cannot be moved unless the breech is completely closed.

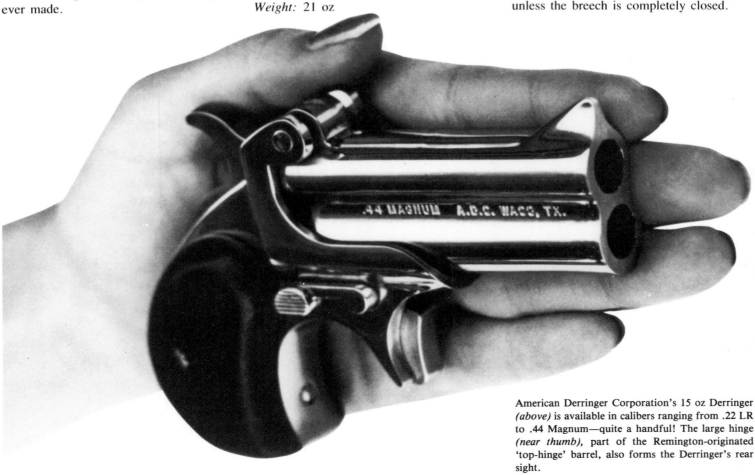

American Derringer Corporation's 15 oz Derringer *(above)* is available in calibers ranging from .22 LR to .44 Magnum—quite a handful! The large hinge *(near thumb)*, part of the Remington-originated 'top-hinge' barrel, also forms the Derringer's rear sight.

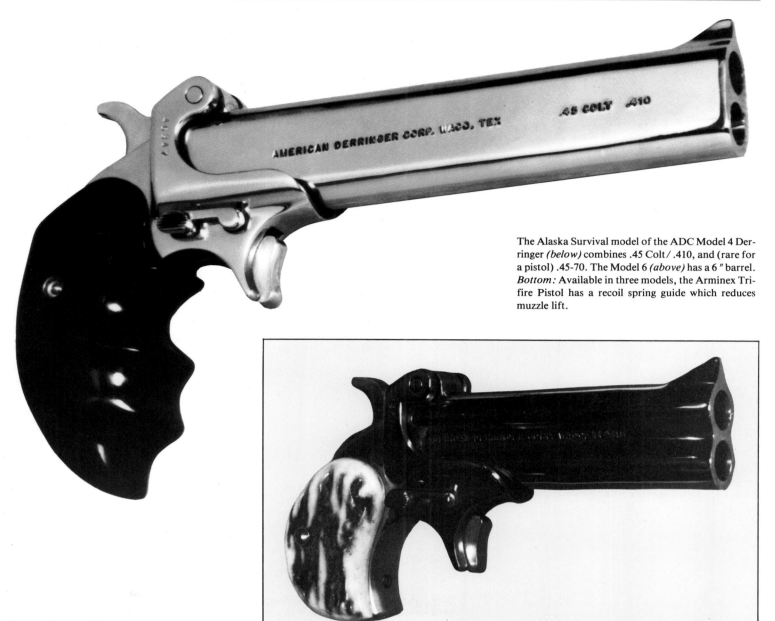

The Alaska Survival model of the ADC Model 4 Derringer *(below)* combines .45 Colt / .410, and (rare for a pistol) .45-70. The Model 6 *(above)* has a 6″ barrel. *Bottom:* Available in three models, the Arminex Trifire Pistol has a recoil spring guide which reduces muzzle lift.

Arminex Ltd.

Trifire Pistol (1911 Based)

Type: Single-action semi-automatic
Caliber: .45ACP, 9mm, .38 Super
Barrel Length: 5″ Standard / Presentation
    models; 6″ Target model
Weight: 38 oz
Finish: Blue steel
Magazine Capacity: Standard 1911
    magazines for each caliber

Arminex's **Trifire** is made available in **Standard**, **Presentation** and **Target** models. The Standard Trifire has a 5″ barrel, standard length slide, and adjustable sights. The Presentation model is distinguished by its ambidextrous safety and burl wooden grips. The Target Trifire has all the features of the Standard model with a 6″ barrel.

All Trifire pistols have a non-hammer dropping, manually operated firing pin lock safety, extra-wide trigger, modified extended slide stop that is easily reached by right- and left-hand shooters, and a recoil spring guide for accuracy and reduced muzzle lift.

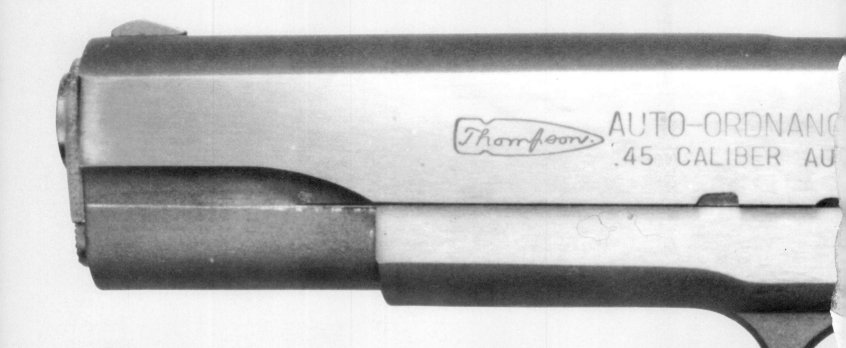

Auto-Ordnance Corp.

Auto-Ordnance 1911A1 Government Model Pistol
Type: Automatic
Caliber: .45ACP, 9mm, .38 Super
Barrel Length: 5″
Weight: 35.5 oz
Grips: 4140 steel with blue finish
Carefully designed to the same specifications as the standard military model, all Auto-Ordnance **1911A1** parts are interchangeable with other government 1911 pistols. The slide's sight plane and the frame's radius are in an anti-glare finish and both grips are detailed with a specially designed Auto-Ordnance medallion. Additional calibers such as 9mm Steyr and 30 Cal. Mauser are being added to the line.

Beretta USA

Beretta 92 F Pistol
Type: Semi-automatic
Caliber: 9mm parabellum
Barrel Length: 4.92″
Weight: 40.89 oz
Length: 8.54″ overall
Finish: Steel coated with a nonreflective matte finish
Sights: Front and rear
Magazine Capacity: 15 rounds
The Beretta **92 F** is a 9mm parabellum semi-automatic pistol designed for military use. Key specifications include a fixed rear sight,

Above and left: The Auto-Ordnance 1911A1 Government Model Pistol is designed to the same specifications as the standard US military model made famous by Colt Industries, and is replete with slide lock *(above trigger)*, thumb safety *(at rear of receiver)* and grip safety *(on backstrap)*. The 'Thompson' logo seen on the slide evidences the fact that Auto-Ordnance was founded by John Thompson and continues to produce the Thompson Submachine Gun.

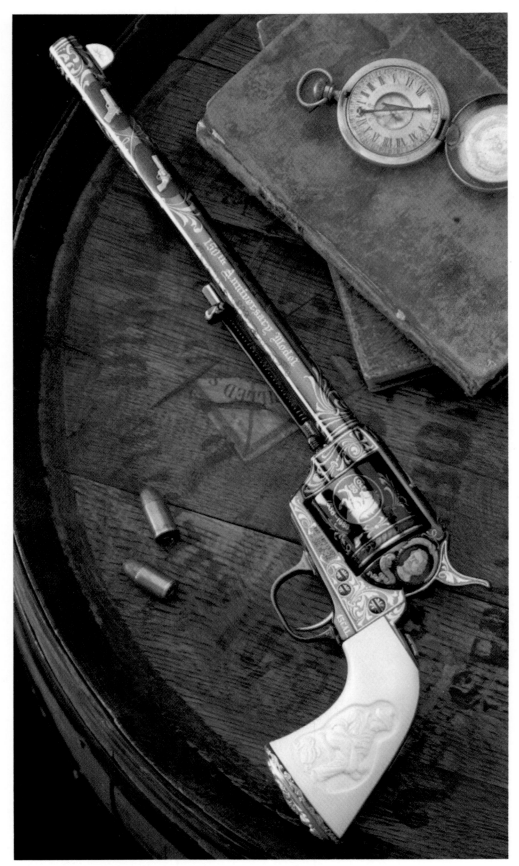

driftable for windage, and a manually operated slide stop that holds the slide open after the last round has been fired. Additional features are the ambidextrous safety, disassembling latch to allow swift field-stripping, firing pin blocking device that prevents accidental misfiring, and an open slide design that eliminates malfunctions due to jamming.

Browning

Buck Mark 22 Pistol
Type: Semi-automatic, blowback
Caliber: .22 LR
Barrel Length: 5.5"
Weight: 32 oz
Length: 9.5" overall
Finish: Matte blue
Magazine Capacity: 10 rounds
Manufactured in Salt Lake City, Browning's **Buck Mark 22** features a 5.5" bull barrel, sights adjustable for windage and elevation and a muzzle recessed to preserve accuracy. Other **Buck Mark** features include the thumb-operated magazine release, slide finger grips, large thumb safety, and black molded composite grips with a skipline checkering pattern.

Bushmaster Firearms

Bushmaster Steel Receiver Pistol
Type: Semi-automatic
Caliber: .223
Barrel Length: 11.5"
Weight: 84 oz
Length: 20.5" overall
Magazine Capacity: 30 rounds
The Bushmaster **Steel Receiver Pistol** has a steel alloy upper receiver and a one-piece welded steel alloy bolt carrier assembly. The front and rear sights are raised and it has an effective range of 250 meters.

Chipmunk Manufacturing, Inc

Chipmunk Silhouette Pistol
Type: Single shot bolt action
Caliber: .22
Barrel Length: 14.88"
Weight: 32 oz
Stock: Walnut rear grip

Colt Industries

Colt MKIV/Series 80 Pistol (Standard 1911A1)
Type: O Frame, semi-automatic
Caliber: .45 ACP
Barrel Length: 5" Government Model;
    3.63" Officer's Model
Weight: 38 oz Government; 34 oz Officer's
    steel, 24 oz Officer's light-weight

The one-of-a-kind Colt 150th Anniversary Exhibition Gun *(above)* is fittingly based on Colt's most famous firearm—the Single Action Army Revolver, aka the 'Peacemaker' of the Wild West—and is chambered for .45 caliber, one of Colt's most famous calibers. Starting with the grips, engravings feature the young seaman Sam Colt whittling the prototype from which the modern revolver would evolve; a head portrait of Samuel Colt *on the receiver flange;* the Colt firearms' 'rampant colt' logo *on the cylinder;* and *on the Buntline-length barrel,* a portrait of Colt's Python Ultimate revolver, one of Colt's most recent designs, and a portrait of Colt's Officers ACP, a contemporary version of the famed 1911 Government model. *Opposite-above, lower left and lower right:* The pistol butt of the 150th Anniversary Gun; receiver section of same; and a 'flip side' view with engravings.

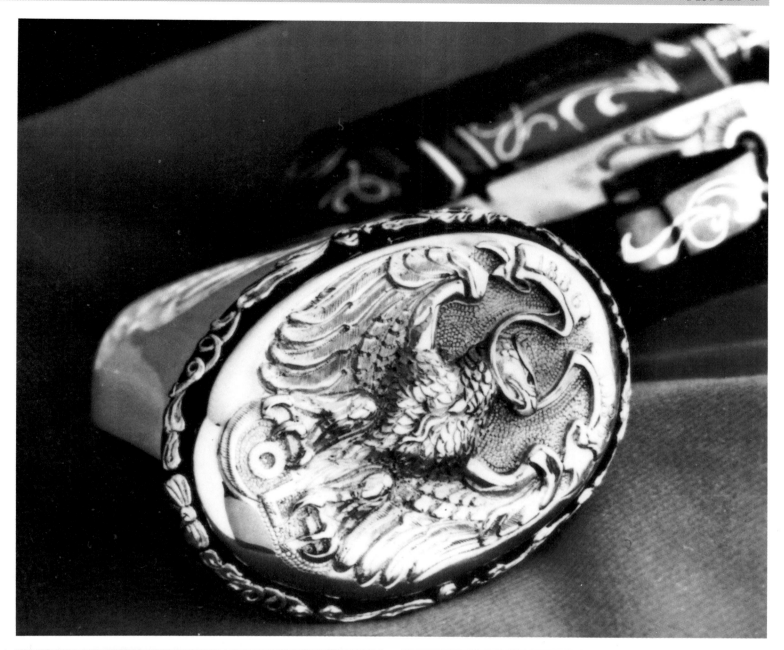

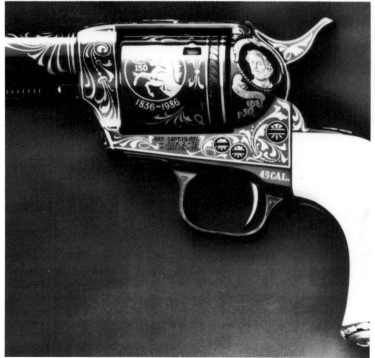

Length: 8.38″ overall Government; 7.25″ overall Officer's

Finish: Stainless steel Government; Stainless steel, matte blue all steel, and matte blue Officer's lightweight

Magazine Capacity: 7 rounds Government; 6 rounds Officer's

Colt's **Government** model 1911A1 with firing pin safety also features a high-profile, fixed front and rear combat-sight system. The basic Government model is available in three different calibers: .45 ACP, 9mm Luger, and .38 Super, the latter two being an ounce heavier in weight and possessing a 9-round magazine capacity. All three calibers of the basic model feature the Colt 'Accurizor' barrel and bushing assembly for increased accuracy.

The compact, highly concealable **Officer's** model has found its popularity with law enforcement and security professionals who require .45 ACP knockdown power in a smaller package. Available in stainless steel, all steel, and lightweight alloy variations, the Officer's model incorporates the same internal firing pin safety as the Government model. Sights are fixed: ramp blade with white dot front, square notch with two white dots rear.

To celebrate Colt's 150 year anniversary, a limited edition **Officer's 45 ACP Ultimate** with rosewood grips and Colt anniversary medallion were offered with a 'Double Diamond' rollmark and matching serial numbers.

A more refined version of the standard 1911A1 is Colt's **Combat Government** model featuring a flat mainspring housing, long trigger, beveled magazine well, front grip serrations, and lowered improved ejection port. The .45 ACP Combat is comparable in size and weight to the basic Government model but is distinguished by its sights. The front sight is undercut to give a sharper picture, and the rear is a fixed white outline square notch sight to highlight the target and viewing picture.

The **Combat Elite** model is a highly specialized 1911 .45 ACP automatic that has been designed to provide a more competition-ready pistol to modern combat-style match shooters. Measuring to the specs of the Combat Government model, the Elite features a high profile front and rear sight with three dot sighting for quick sight alignment, extended-grip safety, positive ejection port, and stainless receiver.

Colt's **Combat Commander** has an all steel frame of 7.75″ overall (4.25″ barrel) to make it easily concealable. Available in .45 ACP, 9mm Luger, and .38 Super calibers, it weighs in at 37 oz (45 ACP) and 36 oz (9mm .38 Super). The .45 version holds the standard 7 rounds; the 9mm and .38 Super have magazine capacities of 9 rounds each. The Combat Commander incorporates Colt's 'Gold Cup' feed ramp for improved feeding of all ammunition brands and a lower ejection port. Its sights are fixed: ramp style blade front and fixed square notch rear.

The **Gold Cup National Match** completes the MKIV/Series 80 of 45 ACP Government models. A centerfire target pistol with accurizor barrel and bushing that tightens shot groupings as much as 90%, the Gold Cup National Match is sized a standard 8.5″ overall (5″ barrel) and weighs in at 39 oz. Special features include its wide-grooved trigger with adjustable stop, serrated target hammer, and flat backstrap mainspring housing. The front sight is undercut to allow a clear, sharp view and the rear sight is adjustable for height and windage. Like the Government model, the Gold Cup can also be converted to .22 LR or 9mm calibers.

Colt .380 Automatic Pistol

Type: O Frame, semi-automatic

Caliber: .380 ACP

Barrel Length: 3.29″ Government model; 2.75″ Mustang model

Weight: 21.8 oz Government; 18.5 oz Mustang

Length: 6.15″ overall Government; 5.5″ overall Mustang

Finish: Blue, electroless nickel, bright nickel Government; blue Mustang

Magazine Capacity: 7 rounds Government; 5 rounds Mustang

Left: These two highly polished stainless steel pistols were offered in a matched set, each bearing the logo 'Double Diamond' to commemorate Colt's 150th Anniversary. The set is comprised of a 6″ barrel .357 Magnum Colt Python Ultimate Revolver and a Colt Officers ACP, bearing matching serial numbers and cased with a 150th Anniversary Medallion in a custom-fitted case. Both pistols have rosewood grips. The Python is considered to be one of the world's finest production revolvers. *Above:* Colt's Gold Cup National Match is based on the 1911 Government model, but is equipped with an Accurizor barrel, adjustable rear sight and adjustable trigger stop. *Below:* The Colt Mark IV Series 80 Government model 1911A1 has an Accurizor barrel and is available in three calibers.

Colt's **.380 Government** pistol is a scaled-down version of the 1911-A1 Colt Government Model. It incorporates the use of a firing pin safety that allows the carrying of a round in the chamber in a 'cocked and locked' mode. Other features: sight radius of 4.2″, fixed ramp blade front sight and fixed square notch rear sight.

The **Mustang** is a smaller and lighter version of the Government model that combines the same standard features and maintains the knock-down power of its Government counterpart (four times that of a .22 or .25 caliber pistol).

Also available in a limited edition version, the **Mustang 380 First Edition** matches the specs of the regulation Mustang except in barrel length (2.73″), overall length (5.6″), and its presentation (rosewood grips with gold Colt medallions). Each of the First Edition Mustangs is serial numbered from 1 to 1000 and accompanied by a walnut presentation case that has been fitted with velvet.

Colt Python .357 Revolver

Type: I Frame, double action
Caliber: .357 Magnum
Barrel Length: 2.5″, 4″, 6″, and 8″
Weight: 38 oz with a standard 4″ barrel
Length: 9.25″ overall with a standard 4″ barrel
Finish: All barrel lengths available in blue; 4″ and 6″ lengths also available in stainless and Ultimate (highly polished stainless) steel; 2.5″ also available in Ultimate stainless steel
Cylinder Capacity: 6 rounds

Above from the top: The Colt Peacekeeper is a medium frame .357 Magnum revolver with a non-glare matte blue combat finish. Colt 'gripper' combat grips and the choice of either 4″ or 6″ barrel length. The Colt Python .357 Magnum revolver is available in barrel lengths of 2.5″ (shown here), 4″, 6″ and 8″. Colt's Mustang 380 is .5″ shorter and .5″ less in height than the standard 380 Government model, and can be tucked away 'as neatly as most .25 autos.' *Opposite:* A limited edition Mustang 380 and its spec sheet. Spec sheets and Historical Letters on various Colt firearms are available from the company.

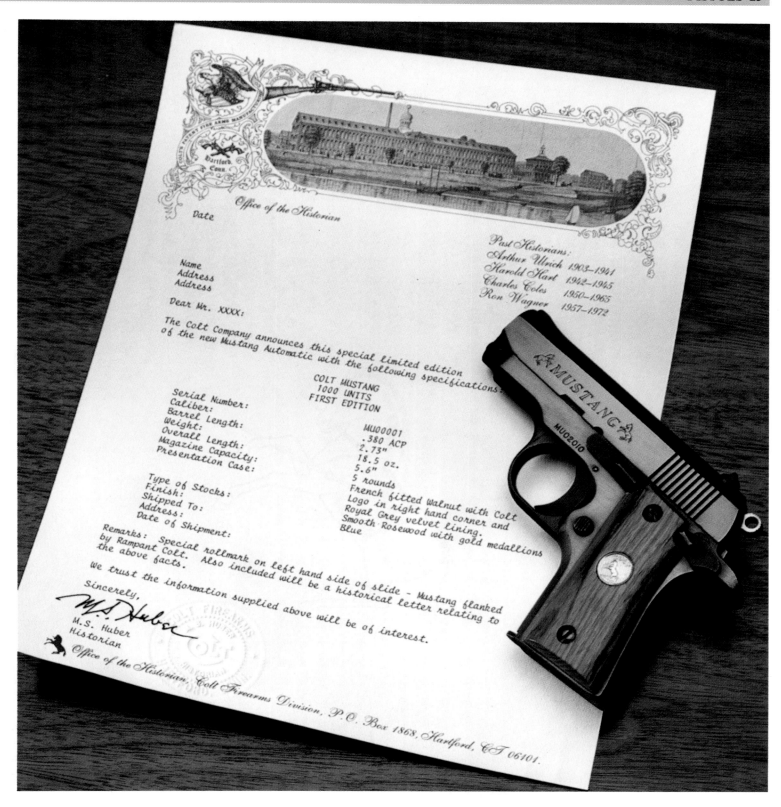

The Colt Company announces this special limited edition of the new Mustang Automatic with the following specifications:

COLT MUSTANG
1000 UNITS
FIRST EDITION

Serial Number: MU00001
Caliber: .380 ACP
Barrel Length: 2.73"
Weight: 18.5 oz.
Overall Length: 5.6"
Magazine Capacity: 5 rounds
Presentation Case: French fitted walnut with Colt Logo in right hand corner and Royal Grey velvet lining.

Type of Stocks: Smooth Rosewood with gold medallions
Finish: Blue

Remarks: Special rollmark on left hand side of slide - Mustang flanked by Rampant Colt. Also included will be a historical letter relating to the above facts.

Since its introduction in 1955, the Colt **Python** has been considered one of the world's finest all-around production revolvers. All contact points are hand-honed and fitted and its vent rib and extended ejector rod housing have created a classic Python look enjoyed by hunters, target shooters, and law enforcement officers. Special features include a locking hand which secures the cylinder in place when firing and a fast cocking wide-spur hammer.

Commemorating Colt's 150 year anniversary, a limited edition **Double Diamond Python Ultimate** (1986 availability) combines the 6″ barrel revolver with rosewood grips and the Colt anniversary medallion.

Colt .357 Revolvers
Trooper MK V, Peacekeeper, and
King Cobra Models

Type: Double action
Caliber: .357 Magnum
Barrel Length: 4″ and 6″ versions with full-length ejector rod shroud
Weight: 42 oz (4″ barrel); 46 oz (6″ barrel)
Length: 9.13″ (4″ barrel); 11.13″ (6″ barrel)
Finish: Blue or nickel (Trooper MK V); Matte blue (Peacekeeper); Stainless steel (King Cobra)
Cylinder Capacity: 6 rounds

In addition to the Python, Colt's .357 Magnum offerings come in three variations: the **Trooper MK V**, a rugged law enforcement service revolver, the **Peacekeeper** medium frame revolver with non-glare combat finish, and the 1986 edition stainless steel **King Cobra**. All three guns have a solid barrel rib

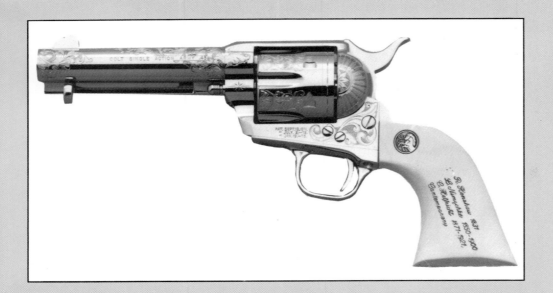

Right: The Texas Sesquicentennial engravings, ivory grips and special plating on these single action Colt .45 Long Colt Sheriff's models were provided by the Colt Custom Shop, which offers various products and services to customers who wish to personalize and adorn their firearms. The particular firearms depicted *here* are actual 1986 commemorative editions produced by—and available from—Colt's custom shop: *at top of photo* is the Texas Premier edition, and *below it* is the Texas Deluxe edition. *Above:* Colt's 150th Anniversary Engraving Sampler was available on any current blue or nickel finish gun only during Colt's 150th Anniversary year, 1986. It featured custom ivory grips and the four most popular engraving styles in Colt's history—Henshaw, Nimschke, Helfricht and Colt Contemporary (*note* calligraphy on the pistol's grips)—blended tastefully, with each style devoted to a particular part of the gun. *Below:* If he means business, he'd better have that thing cocked! The Colt single action would otherwise just let him pull that trigger until doomsday, without firing a shot. The single action eventually did give way to the hammer-cocking trigger mechanism of the double action, and they made films of the good old days. Shown *here* is Marty Robins in Parade Pictures' 1963 *Ballad of a Gunfighter.*

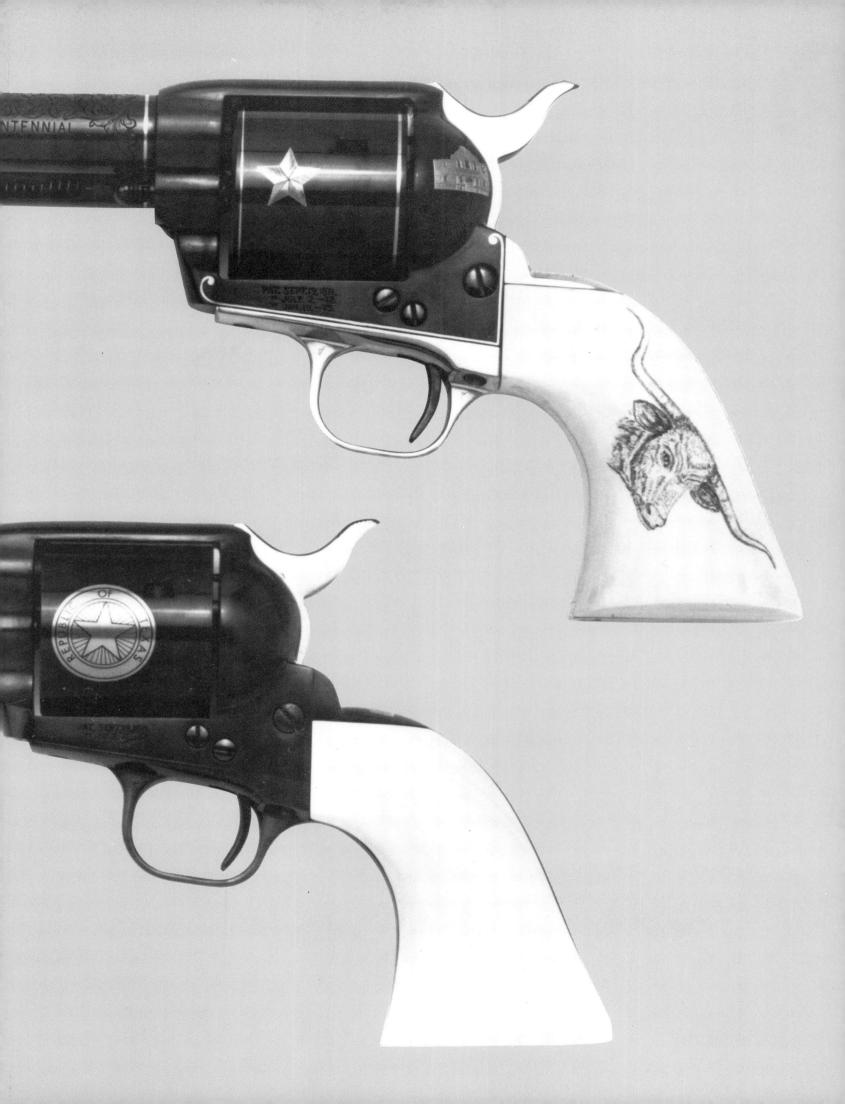

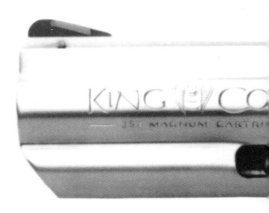

for quick sight alignment and balance, white-outline adjustable rear sights, and a red insert front sight for low light conditions. The Trooper MK V comes with standard checkered walnut grips; the Peacekeeper and King Cobra sport rubber grips.

Colt .38 Special Revolvers
Detective Special, Commando Special, and Agent Models

Type: D-Frame, double-action
Caliber: .38 Special
Barrel Length: 2″ all models; 3″ Detective; 4″ Commando
Weight: 21.5 oz 2″ Detective and Commando, 16.75 oz Agent; 23.5 oz 3″ Detective; 25.5 oz 4″ Commando
Length: 6.88″ overall (all 2″ barrel models); 7.88″ Detective (3″ barrel); 8.88″ Commando (4″ barrel)
Finish: Blue or bright nickel—Detective; non-glare matte blue—Commando and Agent models
Cylinder Capacity: 6 rounds

A standard 2″ revolver for off-duty and plain clothes police officers, the **Detective Special** has been in production since 1927. Its advantages include the locking hand that secures cylinder in place when firing, fixed ramp style front sight, highly polished finish and wrap-around checkered walnut grips. The **Commando Special** combines all the same features in a low-lustre finish with rubber combat grips for law enforcement purposes. The aluminum alloy frame **Agent** model completes the trio in only 16.75 oz, with matte blue finish and walnut grips.

Colt Diamondback Revolver

Type: D Frame, double-action
Caliber: .22 Long Rifle, .38 Special
Barrel Length: 4″ and 6″
Weight: 31.75 oz and 37.5 oz (4″ and 6″ barrel 22s); 27.5 oz and 34 oz (4″ and 6″ barrel 38s)
Length: 9″ (4″ barrel models); 11″ (6″ barrel models)

Left, above: Examples of the decorative art of the Colt Custom Shop include a revolver *(top of photo)* done in Colt's American-style Scroll engraving, and an automatic featuring Colt's Oakleaf-style Scroll. *Left, below:* This .357 Magnum Python revolver is engraved in Colt's 'American-style' and is shown with a Colt Historical Letter on its background as an individual firearm. *Above:* The Colt stainless steel .357 Magnum revolver features barrel lengths of 4" or 6", adjustable rear sight and moderate price tag. The Colt Detective Special *(below)* with its 3" barrel has been a favorite for plainclothes policemen since 1927. *Below right:* Of the same design as the Detective Special, Colt's Agent model features an aluminum alloy frame and matte blue finish.

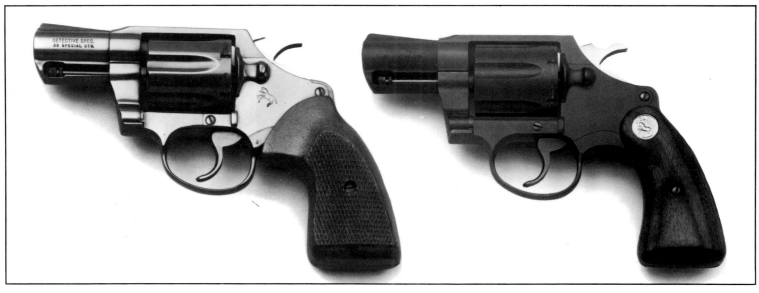

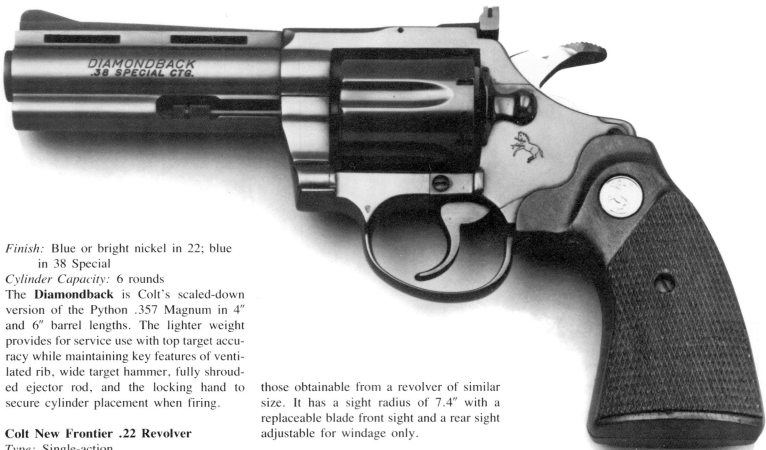

Finish: Blue or bright nickel in 22; blue in 38 Special

Cylinder Capacity: 6 rounds

The **Diamondback** is Colt's scaled-down version of the Python .357 Magnum in 4″ and 6″ barrel lengths. The lighter weight provides for service use with top target accuracy while maintaining key features of ventilated rib, wide target hammer, fully shrouded ejector rod, and the locking hand to secure cylinder placement when firing.

Colt New Frontier .22 Revolver

Type: Single-action

Caliber: .22 LR

Barrel Length: 4.75″, 6″ and 7.5″

Weight: 29.5 oz, 31 oz and 33 oz for barrel lengths above

Length: 9.5″, 11.5″ and 12.75″ overall for barrel lengths above

Finish: Blue

Cylinder Capacity: 6 rounds

The **New Frontier .22** is a scaled down version of the famous Colt single action army revolver. Available in three barrel lengths, the New Frontier has an adjustable rear sight, high ramp front sight, and cross bolt safety.

Coonan Arms, Inc

Coonan Model B .357 Magnum

Type: Locked breech semi-automatic

Caliber: .357 Magnum

Barrel Length: 5″

Weight: 42 oz

Length: 8.3″ overall

Grips: Matte/polished stainless steel

Magazine Capacity: 7 in magazine, 1 in chamber

Based on the Colt/Browning design and chambering the standard .357 Magnum cartridge, Coonan Arms' powerful automatic pistol has replaced an earlier style swinging link and link pin with a barrel lug and cam arrangement to effect locking and unlocking of the pistol's barrel and slide. This self-loading pistol with its .357 Magnum cartridge develops velocities far higher than

those obtainable from a revolver of similar size. It has a sight radius of 7.4″ with a replaceable blade front sight and a rear sight adjustable for windage only.

Dan Wesson Arms

Dan Wesson .22 Rimfire Revolver

Type: Six shot double and single action

Caliber: .22 LR (models 22 and 722); .22 Win Mag (models 22M and 722M)

Barrel Length: 2.5″, 4″, 6″, 8″

Weight: 40 oz (4″ barrel)

Length: 9.25″ overall (4″ barrel)

Finish: Brite blue (22 and 22M); satin stainless steel (722 and 722M)

Cylinder Capacity: 6 rounds

Dan Wesson .22 target guns are built on a .357 Magnum frame to give the gun balance. Any of the four barrel lengths available can be substituted at any time. Features include the wide spur (.38″) hammer with short double action travel, smooth, wide-tang (.38″) trigger with overtravel adjustment, and interchangeable blade front and rear sights.

Dan Wesson .32 Magnum Revolver

Type: Six shot double and single action

Caliber: .32 Magnum

Barrel Length: 2.5″, 4″, 6″, 8″

Weight: 39 oz (4″ barrel)

Length: 9.25″ overall (4″ barrel)

Finish: Brite blue and satin stainless steel

Cylinder Capacity: 6 rounds

Best suited for target and small game, the **.32 Magnum** offers a high muzzle velocity and provides a flat trajectory that increases accuracy. The front sight is a serrated, interchangeable blade with a red insert standard. The rear sight is an interchangeable

blade for wide or narrow notch sight picture, adjustable for windage and elevation.

Dan Wesson .38 Special Revolver

Type: Six shot double and single action

Caliber: .38 Special hi-speed and mid-range

Barrel Length: 2.5″, 4″, 6″; Target model also available with 8″ barrel

Weight: 34 oz (4″ barrel) Service model; 36 oz (4″ barrel) Target model

Length: 9.25″ overall (4″ barrel)

Finish: Blue and satin stainless steel

Cylinder Capacity: 6 rounds

Interchangeable barrel assemblies and grips make the Dan Wesson **.38 Special** a versatile weapon for law enforcement and target gun for sportsmen. Other standard features include a wide-tang trigger and wide spur hammer. Sight specifications vary depending on **Service** or **Target** model applications.

Dan Wesson .357 Magnum Revolver

Type: Six shot double and single action

Caliber: .357 Magnum, .38 Special

Barrel Length: 2.5″, 4″, 6″

Weight: 34 oz (4″ barrel) Service model; 36 oz (4″ barrel) Target model

Length: 9.25″ overall (4″ barrel)

Finish: Blue and satin stainless steel

Cylinder Capacity: 6 rounds

A versatile gun with the capability to substitute barrel lengths and grips to meet

The small frame of Colt's Diamondback *(left)* fits most shooter's hands. The Coonan Arms autoloader *(above)* translates more of its .357 Magnum power to muzzle velocity than most other autos, due to its improved slide locking mechanism. Dan Wesson's .357 Magnum revolver has quick-change auxiliary barrels *(see box)*; *below* is a cutaway view of a Dan Wesson SuperMagnum model's barrel structure.

changing needs, Dan Wesson offers the **.357 Magnum** with interchangeable assemblies that include barrel lengths of 8″, 10″, 12″ and 15″. Suitable for law enforcement, protection, or target shooting purposes, the rear sight is a patented, interchangeable blade for wide or narrow notch sight picture.

Dan Wesson .357/.375 SuperMag Revolvers

Type: Six shot double and single action
Caliber: .357 Maximum and .375 SuperMag
Barrel Length: 6″, 8″, 10″
Weight: 62 oz (8″ barrel)
Length: 14.38″ overall (8″ barrel)
Finish: Brite blue; satin stainless steel (.357 Model only)
Cylinder Capacity: 6 rounds

Dan Wesson Arms' **.357 SuperMag** offers all the power and accuracy of a .357 Magnum in brite blue (**Model 40**) and stainless steel (**Model 740**) finishes. Its unique slotted shroud dissipates heat which in turn reduces the chance of heat distortion. For optimum

range and field accuracy, the front sight is a serrated, interchangeable blade with red insert standard. The rear sight is also an interchangeable blade for wide or narrow

notch sight pictures, adjustable for windage and elevation both. The **.375 Supermag** possesses the same characteristics as the .357 and is offered with the brite blue finish.

Dan Wesson pistols feature the 'Pistol Pac' *(above)* system of quickly interchangeable barrel lengths. Depicted *here* is the Dan Wesson .357/.375 Super-Magnum with ventilated barrel shroud, which greatly reduces the chance for heat distortion. Detonics' Combat Master *(above opposite)* in .45 ACP is more compact than the standard 1911A1 model pistol, yet retains a good weight-to-recoil ratio. The FIE D86 Derringer *(below opposite)* features an automatic internal transfer bar firing system system for safety, and a built-in spare ammo compartment and safety grip.

Dan Wesson .41/.44 Magnum Revolver
Type: Six shot double and single action
Caliber: .41 Magnum (models 41, 741);
     .44 Magnum and .44 Special
    (models 44, 744)
Barrel Length: 4″, 6″, 8″, 10″
Weight: 53 oz (6″ barrel)
Length: 12″ overall (6″ barrel)
Finish: Brite blue and satin stainless steel
Cylinder Capacity: 6 rounds

Designs newly pioneered by Dan Wesson Arms, the **.41 and .44 Magnum** models are intended for serious big game and other targets. Both guns are constructed of strong one-piece frames and the .44 is available with an optional, patented 'power control' feature in 4″, 6″, and 8″ barrel lengths. The Dan Wesson 'power control' reduces muzzle flip to keep the target in the picture for follow-up shots.

Detonics

Detonics Combat Master Pistol

Type: Single action
Caliber: .45 ACP
Barrel Length: 3.5"
Weight: 29 oz
Length: 6.75" overall
Finish: Stainless steel
Magazine Capacity: 6 plus one chambered
The **Combat Master** is Detonics' smallest single action production .45 ACP. It sports a beveled magazine well, full-clip indicator, throated barrel and polished feed ramp, and a sloped slide for fast hammer cocking. Among its special features are the Detonics self-centering bull style barrel that returns the locking mechanism to its original position after each shot, and the captured multiple-spring recoil system which eases assembly and lessens the risk of fly-away springs. The Combat Master is available in three different surface finishes with varying sight configurations.

Detonics Pocket 9 Pistol

Type: Double and single action
Caliber: 9mm parabellum
Barrel Length: 3"
Weight: 26 oz
Length: 5.75" overall
Finish: Stainless steel
Magazine Capacity: 6 plus one chambered
Touted as 'ultimately concealable' and the world's smallest production double action 9mm parabellum, the **Pocket 9** is constructed of stainless steel with a blow-back action and ambidextrous firing pin safety. Designed for home defense and law enforcement, other features include its hooked and serrated trigger guard, snag-free hammer, and captive recoil spring.

Detonics Scoremaster Pistol

Type: Semi-automatic
Caliber: .45 ACP or .451 Detonics Magnum
Barrel Length: 5", 6"
Weight: 42 oz (5" barrel); 43 oz (6" barrel)
Length: 9" overall (5" barrel); 10" overall (6" barrel)
Finish: Match-grade stainless steel
Magazine Capacity: 7 plus one chambered
The Detonics **Scoremaster** is a full-size production model semi-automatic designed for combat shooting matches. This pistol features a Detonics bull style, self-centering barrel with recessed target crown and dual-spring recoil system that insures the return of the locking mechanism to exactly the same position after each shot. The rear sights are adjustable match-grade, and the front sights interchangeable between the three provided: white, fluorescent orange and serrated black ramp. The mainspring housing, extended beavertail grip safety and wraparound rubber grips are all Pachmayr.

Detonics Servicemaster Pistol

Caliber: .45 ACP
Barrel Length: 5.25"; 4.25" (Servicemaster II)
Weight: 32 oz
Length: 7.88" overall
Finish: Non-glare matte; polished slide with matte satin (Servicemaster II)
Sights: Fixed combat
Magazine Capacity: 7 plus one chambered
Servicemaster and **Servicemaster II** (with shortened barrel) are Detonics' well balanced, highly accurate service weapons. Handfitted parts of stainless steel go into the composition of this handgun which also features Detonics' patented bushingless barrel and counter-wound dual spring recoil systems.

Feather Enterprises

Feather Enterprises Mini-AT Semi-automatic Pistol

Type: Semi-automatic Pistol
Caliber: 22 LR
Barrel Length: 5.5"
Weight: 1.95 lbs
Magazine Capacity: 20 rounds
The **Mini-AT** is a very sophisticated pistol: 'AT' stands for 'Advanced Technology.' Accessories available for the Mini-At include sling and swivels, a 'no-gunsmithing' scope mount, padded carrying case, replacement barrels and more.

FIE

D86 Derringer

Type: Single action
Caliber: .38 Special
Barrel Length: 3"

Reproductions of the famous Colt single action six shooter, the FIE Texas Ranger *(left and below)* and Little Ranger *(below left)* revolvers feature floating firing pins, hammer block safety mechanisms and manufacture to modern standards. They are available in .22 Short, Long or Long Rifle, and .22 Magnum calibers. The Little Ranger has a 3.25″ barrel, and the Texas Ranger has optional barrel lengths. The FIE Titan II *(right)* is a compact, easy-to-take-down .22 LR autoloader with a 10-shot magazine capacity.

Weight: 11 oz
Finish: 'Dyna-chrome' hard matte finish
Sights: Fixed

The **Model D86 Derringer** possesses an automatic internal transfer bar firing system that makes it one of the safest derringers available. FIE's Model D86 preserves the Remington-designed bird's-head safety grip and top-hinged barrel, integral sights, exposed single action hammer and spur trigger. In addition, it features a built-in compartment for storing a spare round of ammunition.

Texas Ranger Revolver
Type: Single action
Caliber: .22 LR or .22 Magnum Combo
Barrel Length: 3.25″ (Little Ranger Model); 4.75″, 6.5″, 9″ (standard model)
Weight: 31 oz to 37 oz
Finish: Blue
Sights: Blade front; fixed rear
Cylinder Capacity: 6 rounds

The **Texas Ranger and Little Ranger** revolvers are reproductions of the 'gun that won the West' with custom blued finish and hand-rubbed walnut grips. The clean Old West look is subtly but stylishly enhanced with three 24kt gold plated decorative accents. Manufactured to modern standards, the Texas Ranger models also feature a floating firing pin, fluted cylinder, and an exclusive hammer block safety system.

Titan II .22 LR Pistol
Type: Semi-automatic
Caliber: .22 LR
Barrel Length: 3.88″
Weight: 25.75 oz
Length: 6.75″ overall
Finish: Bright blue
Sights: Drift adjustable
Magazine Capacity: 10 rounds

FIE's **Titan II** has a fast, easy take-down system with disconnecting trigger, hammer, firing pin block and magazine. Standard grips are black with diamond checkering; wood optional.

Titan Tiger Revolver
Type: Double action
Caliber: .38 Special

Barrel Length: 2″, 4″
Finish: Bright blue
Sights: Ramp front; fixed rear
Cylinder Capacity: 6 rounds

Titan Tiger revolvers are manufactured in the United States using design components furnished by the Weihrauch Co of Germany. Available with 2″ and 4″ barrel lengths, the Titan Tiger is a compact gun suitable for law enforcement, security, or sportsman applications. Grips are walnut.

Freedom Arms

Freedom Arms .454 Casull Revolver

Type: Single-action
Caliber: .454 Casull–45 Colt–44 Rem Mag
Barrel Length: 4.75″, 6″, 7.5″, 10″, 12″
Weight: 50 oz (7.5″ barrel)
Length: 14″ overall (7.5″ barrel)
Finish: Brushed stainless
Sights: Notched rear; blade front
Cylinder Capacity: 5 rounds

Dick Casull calls his handgun the 'world's most powerful revolver,' and Jan Libourel in *Guns and Ammo* has further labeled this super-powered .45 Magnum a revolver that's 'slick as a Ferrari and tough as a tank.' Constructed of stainless steel, the **.454 Casull** is capable of firing a bullet with velocities of 850 to 2000 fps—nearly twice that

of a .44 Magnum. The revolver features a patented sliding bar safety system, separate from the trigger, allowing a clean trigger pull to match its long range accuracy.

Freedom Arms .22 Mini Revolver

Type: Single-action
Caliber: .22 LR, .22 Magnum, .22 Percussion
Barrel Length: 1″, 1.75″, 3″
Weight: 4 oz (1″ barrel)
Finish: Stainless steel
Sights: Fixed front and rear
Cylinder Capacity: 5 rounds (LR and Percussion); 4 rounds (Magnum)

Despite their size, all Freedom Arms **Mini Revolvers** sport man-size hammer spurs, half cock safeties, and the latest Casull improvements: floating firing pin, positive cylinder pin lockup, simplified action, and

enlarged grips for better control. Highly concealable, these 4- and 5-shot guns are both potent and compact.

Hopkins & Allen Arms

Boot Pistol

Type: Muzzleloading underhammer
Caliber: .36 (New Model); .45 (Original and Target Boot models)
Weight: 2 lbs (New Model); 2.5 lbs (Original and Target)
Length: 12″ overall (New Model); 13″ overall (Original and Target)
Grips: Walnut

Companion pieces to the Hopkins & Allen full line of muzzleloading underhammer rifles, the **Boot Pistol** series features simply designed actions that should provide years of trouble free shooting. The Target Boot Pistol is distinguished by its forend with escutcheon and contained ramrod.

Kentucky Pistol

Type: Muzzleloader
Caliber: .45
Barrel Length: 10″
Weight: 48 oz
Length: 15.5″ overall

In both percussion and flintlock models, the **Kentucky** muzzleloading pistol comes

Dick Casull's Freedom Arms manufactures the .454 Casull (.45 Magnum) Revolver *(left center),* which has supplanted the Smith & Wesson .44 Magnum as the world's most powerful handgun. Freedom Arms also manufactures the very compact Mini Revolver in .22 LR, Magnum and percussion models. Available from the manufacturer is a Mini Revolver concealing belt buckle holster *(above);* and engraving *(below)* for both the .454 Casull and the Mini Revolver.

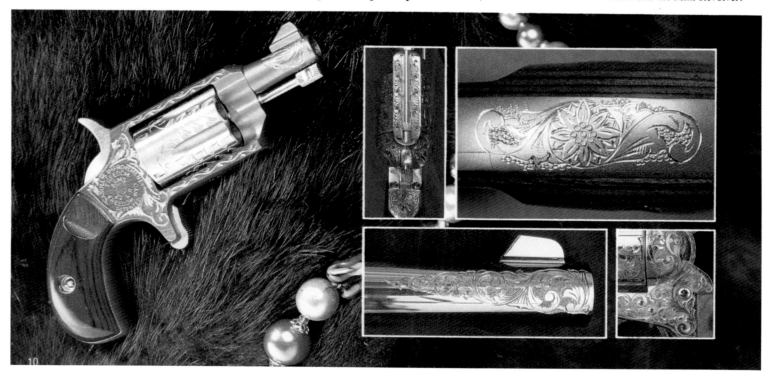

equipped with convertible ignition, heavy duty ramrod and special Hopkins & Allen breech and tang. These guns are also available in kit form.

Iver Johnson's Arms, Inc

Model 50-A Sidewinder
Type: Revolver
Caliber: .22
Barrel Length: 6"
Weight: 31 oz
Grips: Stag
Designed for hunting or plinking, the **Sidewinder** features the Iver Johnson revolver action, wide hammer spur and half-cock safety in a solid frame configuration. All Iver Johnson solid frame revolvers feature the new, extra-wide loading gate for faster, easier loading and clearing of the cylinder.

55-A Target
Type: Revolver
Caliber: .22
Barrel length: 4.5" and 6"
Weight: 30.5 oz in 6" length
The solid frame **55-A Target** model features a clean, crisp action, reliable for hunting or for tending the trap line.

55S-A Cadet
Type: Revolver
Caliber: .22, .32, .38
Barrel Length: 2.5"
Weight: 24 oz
The **55S-A Cadet** is used widely for security work and is of the solid frame configuration.

56-A Starter
Type: Revolver
Caliber: .22, .32 blank cartridges
The **56-A Starter** is a popular starting pistol for athletic contests, theater, sports events or dog training.

57-A Target
Type: Revolver
Caliber: .22
Barrel Length: 4.5" and 6"
Sights: Adjustable
Weight: 30.5 oz in 6" length
In keeping with the Iver Johnson tradition of good quality for a reasonable price, the **57-A Target** model features adjustable sights in a solid-frame configuration.

Model 67 Viking
Type: Top-Break Revolver
Caliber: .22
Barrel Length: 4.5" and 6"
Sights: Fully Adjustable
Weight: 31 oz in 4.5" length and 34 oz in 6" length

The **Model 67 Viking** features fully adjustable sights, Flash Control Cylinder and the famous Iver Johnson Hammer-the-Hammer safety action that bars accidental discharge.

Snub 67S
Type: Top-Break Revolver
Caliber: .22, .32, .38
Barrel Length: 2.75"
Sights: Fully Adjustable
Weight: 25 oz
The **Snub 67S** has the same features as the Model 67 Viking

Trailsman 66
Type: Top-Break Revolver
Caliber: .22
Barrel Length: 6"
Sights: Fully Adjustable
The **Trailsman 66** does not have the Hammer-the-Hammer safety feature, and is available only with the 6" barrel. Otherwise, the Trailsman 66 has the same features as the Model 67 Viking.

Jennings Firearms, Inc

Model J-22 Pistol
Caliber: .22 LR
Barrel Length: 2.5"
Weight: 13 oz
Length: 5" overall
Finish: Black teflon, satin nickel, or bright chrome
Magazine Capacity: 6 rounds
In addition to the completed, test-fired pistol, Jennings **J-22 Pistol** parts may all be ordered separately from this Chino, California company. Available with highly polished, resin-impregnated wood grips, all parts are American made.

Ljutic Industries, Inc

LJII Pistol
Type: Two shot double action
Caliber: .22 Mag
Barrel Length: 2.75"
Sights: Fixed front
Magazine Capacity: 2 rounds
Handcrafted as are all Ljutic weapons, the **LJII** is a double action .22 Mag with a 3.5" grip and a ventilated rib barrel with front sight. The limited-edition grips are made from American and English walnut and finished with fancy checkering.

Ljutic Space Pistol
Caliber: .308 and .357; .22 and .44 Mag
Grips: Natural wood
The Ljutic **Space Pistol** has an in-line design that makes it well-suited to high accuracy target and silhouette shooting. It's available in standard and custom models.

Mitchell Arms

Mitchell Arms Army Model Revolver
Type: Single-action
Caliber: .22 LR, .22 Mag, .357 Mag, .44 Mag, .45 Colt
Barrel Length: 4.75" to 7.5"; 10", 12", 18" (Special Silhouette Model)
Finish: Bright blue
Mitchell Arms **Basic Revolvers** with fixed sights and a second group with adjustable sights range in caliber from .22 LR to .444 Mag and .45 Colt. Barrels range from 4.75" to 7.5" in length. **Dual Cylinder** models with adjustable sights offer the same barrel lengths in calibers ranging from .22 LR to .44 Mag. A **Special Silhouette** model, .44 Mag only, for long range handgunning comes in the longer barrel lengths of 10" to 18".
All Mitchell Arms revolvers incorporate a patented hammer-block safety mechanism in addition to the traditional internal safety notch. They have high grade steel barrels, a forged steel frame, and a solid walnut grip built in the style of the old black powder revolvers.

Spectre Pistol
Type: Double action
Caliber: 9mm
Sights: Adjustable front and rear
Magazine Capacity: 30 and 50 rounds
Mitchell Arms hi-tech **Spectre** is a high capacity rapid fire pistol with a patented 'sinusoidal' rifling which allows the rapid fire without heat build-up. Firing from a closed bolt, the pistol is double-action on the first round and single action semi-automatic on every subsequent round. The same basic features are also available in a Spectre semi-automatic carbine with folding stock.

Navy Arms Company

Classic 'Twister' Pistol
Caliber: .36
Barrel Length: 3.38"
Weight: 24 oz
Length: 7.5" overall
A fabled popular pistol of its day, Navy Arms offers the **Classic Arms 'Twister'** with its over-and-under steel barreled gun. The original model was to have been used by Mississippi gamblers and the like. Navy Arms now produces the replica in kit form.

Duckfoot Pistol
Caliber: .36
Barrel Length: 2.88"
Weight: 32 oz
Length: 10.5" overall
Navy Arms says that the forerunner to this gun was originally a 'swashbuckling' pistol

The Raven Arms Model MP-25 Pistol *(above)* features walnut or simulated ivory grips, nickel, blue or chrome finish, and individual testing on all pistols before their sale to the public.

that could fire six simultaneous shots at a mutinous crew. The replica is sold as a kit or in finished form.

Elgin Cutlass/Pistol
Caliber: .44
Weight: 32 oz
Length: 9″ overall
The **Elgin** is a real collectible. It was the only combination gun (knife and pistol) issued by any of the US military services and the first percussion handgun officially used by the US. The pistol length of 9″ is extended to 12″ total by the blade.

Ethan Allen Pepperbox Pistol
Caliber: .36
Barrel Length: 3.13″
Weight: 40 oz
Length: 9″ overall
Four- and six-shot **Pepperboxes** were originally guns that belonged to the 49ers and the Gold Rush era. This gun was also a forerunner of the 'revolving handgun.'

New Orleans Ace Pistol
Caliber: .44
Barrel Length: 3.5″
Weight: 16 oz
Length: 9″ overall
Navy Arms says that the **Ace Pistol** was the original gamblers' companion, designed in France and made popular by New Orleans gunsmiths in the 1840s. This small replica can be purchased either smoothbore or rifled, finished or in kit form.

Southerner Derringer
Caliber: .44
Barrel Length: 2.5″
Weight: 12 oz
Length: 5″ overall
This pocket pistol is reminiscent of an early derringer used before the days of law and order in the southern United States. Now manufactured by Navy Arms, it is available in finished and kit form.

North American Arms

Mini-Revolvers
Caliber: .22 Short, .22 Long Rifle, .22 WMR
Barrel Lengths: 1.13″, 1.63″ and 2.5″
Finish: Polished satin and matte
The three **Mini-Revolvers** of North American Arms share the same standard features although each chambers a different caliber .22. All feature stainless steel construction, laminated wood grips, blade front design with notched rear sights, ribbed barrel design, and a safety slot where the hammer can rest safely with a fully loaded chamber.
While the .22 Short weighs only 4 oz, the larger .22 Long Rifle weighs only .5 oz more. Each revolver holds five rounds.

Raven Arms

Raven Arms MP-25 Pistol
Type: Automatic
Caliber: .25
Barrel Length: 2.44″
Weight: 15 oz
Length: 4.75″ overall
Finish: Nickel, blue or chrome
Magazine Capacity: 6 rounds
Raven Arms' **MP-25** pistols are entirely made in California of all US parts. Grips are either walnut or simulated ivory and all surfaces are hand polished. Every pistol is test fired prior to its sale.

Remington Arms Company, Inc

Remington Long Range XR-100 Pistol
Type: Bolt action, centerfire, single shot
Caliber: .223 Rem and 7mm BR
Barrel Length: 14.5″
Weight: 66 oz
Length: 21.24″ overall
Grips: 'Zytel' nylon
Ideal for handgun varmint hunting or silhouette shooting, the **XR-100** long-range

The .38 **Chiefs Special** comes in 3 different models all featuring checkered walnut grips with the S&W monogram, a round butt, and serrated ramp front sight with a fixed square notch rear sight. **Model 36** offers these features in a carbon steel body with blue or nickel finish. **Model 37** is the lighter weight version with a frame of aluminum alloy and its cylinder and barrel made of carbon steel. The .38 Chiefs Special Stainless **Model 60** was the first stainless steel handgun. It has a satin finish and is available with just the 2″ barrel. Corresponding weight and length for the stainless steel model are 19 oz and 6.5″ overall.

pistol has a receiver drilled and tapped for scope and other sights. It also features a one piece grip of structural nylon, universal grips, two-position thumb safety switch and match-type grooved trigger.

Serrifile, Inc

Due to an inability to renew their liability insurance, Serrifile, Inc is no longer producing complete rifles and pistols. Production of replacement parts for their **Schuetzen Rifle** and **Terrier One** pistol is, however, ongoing.

Smith & Wesson

Small 'J' Frame Revolvers:
Smith & Wesson Model 31 Regulation Police Revolver

Type: J frame, double action
Caliber: .32 S&W Long
Barrel Length: 2″ and 3″
Weight: 19 oz (2″) and 20 oz (3″)
Length: 6.5″ and 7.5″ overall
Finish: S&W blue or nickel
Cylinder Capacity: 6 rounds
Smith & Wesson's **Model 31** has a square butt, serrated ramp front sight and fixed square notch rear sight. The grips are checkered walnut with S&W monograms.

Smith & Wesson Model 34/63 Kit Gun

Type: J frame, double action revolver
Caliber: .22 LR
Barrel Length: 2″ and 4″; Model 63 with 4″ barrel only
Weight: 22 oz (2″) and 24 oz (4″)
Length: 6.25″ and 8.38″ overall
Finish: S&W blue or nickel (Model 34); satin (Model 63)
Cylinder Capacity: 6 rounds
Ideal for the small hand or the novice target shooter, Smith & Wesson's **Model 34** 1953 (carbon steel) and **Model 63** 1977 (stainless steel) .22/.32 **Kit Guns** have a .375″ semi target hammer and checkered walnut grips. The front sights are serrated ramps and the rear sights are S&W Micrometer Click Sights adjustable for windage and elevation.

Smith & Wesson Model 36/37/60 Chiefs Special Revolver

Type: J frame, double action
Caliber: .38 S&W Special
Barrel Length: 2″ and 3″
Weight: 19.5 oz (Model 36, 2″ barrel); 13.5 oz (Model 37, 2″ barrel)
Length: 6.25″ (Model 36, 2″); 6.31″ (Model 37, 2″) overall
Cylinder Capacity: 5 rounds

Smith & Wesson Model 38/49/649 Bodyguard Revolvers

Type: J frame, double action
Caliber: .38 S&W Special
Barrel Length: 2″
Weight: 14 oz (Model 38); 20 oz (Models 49 and 649)
Length: 6.25″ overall
Finish: S&W blue or nickel (Models 38 and 49); satin (Model 649)
Cylinder Capacity: 5 rounds
All three S&W **Bodyguard** models have serrated ramp front sights and fixed square notch rear sights and they are distinguished by their materials. **Model 38** has an aluminum alloy frame and carbon steel cylinder and barrel. **Model 49** is made of carbon steel, and **Model 649** is made of stainless steel.

Smith & Wesson Model 650/651 Target Kit Guns

Type: J frame, double action revolver
Caliber: .22 Mag and Win
Barrel Length: 3″ (Model 650) and 4″ (Model 651)
Weight: 23 oz (650) and 24.5 oz (651)
Length: 7.25″ and 8.75″ overall
Finish: Satin
Cylinder Capacity: 6 rounds
Target Kit Gun Models 650 and 651 are stainless steel revolvers with checkered walnut grips. **Model 650** has a 3″ heavy barrel and .240″ service hammer. **Model 651** with its 4″ barrel has a .375″ semi-target hammer. Both versions have the S&W red ramp on ramp base front sight and a rear S&W micrometer click sight that is adjustable for windage and elevation.

Medium 'K' Frame Revolvers:
Smith & Wesson Military & Police Revolvers

Type: K frame, double action
Caliber: .38 S&W Special, .357 Magnum
Barrel Length: 2″ to 4″
Weight: 18 oz to 34 oz
Length: 6.88″ to 9.31″ overall

Finish: S&W blue, nickel, or satin
Cylinder Capacity: 6 rounds

All five medium frame S&W **Military & Police Revolvers** have a serrated ramp front sight and a fixed square notch rear sight. They also share the same grip treatment, checkered walnut PC Service with S&W monograms, and the .265″ service hammer and .312″ smooth combat trigger.

The classic favorite of lawmen since its 1899 introduction, the **Model 10** is a carbon steel .38 that is available with barrel lengths of 2″ and 4″ and either a round or square butt. The lightest weight (18 oz with 2″ barrel) **Model 12** is composed of an aluminum alloy frame with carbon steel barrel and cylinder. Preferred by the FBI, the **Model 13** with its 3″ and 4″ heavy barrel choices is available in both .357 Magnum and .38 S&W Special calibers.

The two stainless steel Military & Police models are the **Model 64** which combines .38 caliber with barrel choices of 2″, 3″, and 4″, and the **Model 65** heavy barrel stainless revolver. Model 65 features a choice of .357 Magnum and .38 calibers, and a 3″ heavy barrel version with a round butt or the 4″ heavy barrel version with a square butt.

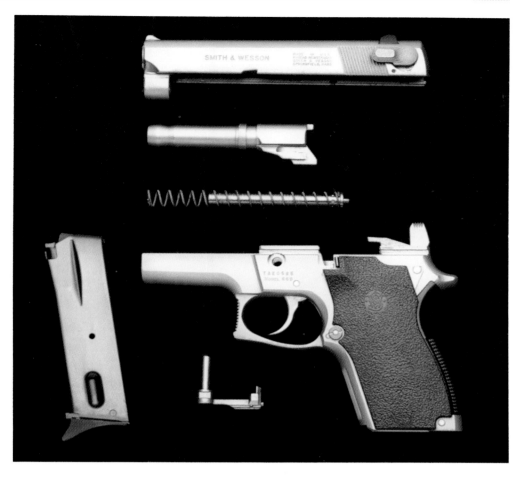

Smith & Wesson Model 15/67 Combat Masterpiece Revolvers

Type: K frame, double action
Caliber: .38 S&W Special
Barrel Length: 2″, 4″, 6″, 8.38″ (Model 67 available with 4″ barrel only)
Weight: 30 oz to 39 oz
Length: 7.25″ to 13.5″ overall
Finish: S&W blue (Model 15); satin (Model 67)
Cylinder Capacity: 6 rounds

Smith & Wesson's **Model 15 Combat Masterpiece** is constructed of carbon steel and is featured with four different barrel lengths. The front sight is a serrated ramp on ramp base (with 2″ and 4″ barrels) and a Patridge sight when combined with the two longer barrel options.

The **Model 67 Combat Masterpiece** is stainless steel and is offered with just the 4″ barrel. The front sight is a S&W red ramp on ramp base. Both Models 15 and 67 have a rear S&W micrometer click sight that is adjustable for windage and elevation, square butt and monogramed checkered walnut grips.

Smith & Wesson Model 17/48 K-22 Masterpiece Revolvers

Type: K frame, double action
Caliber: .22 LR (Model 17); .22 Mag Rim Fire (Model 48)
Barrel Length: 4″, 6″, 8.38″
Weight: 36 oz to 43 oz
Length: 9.25″ to 13.5″ overall
Finish: S&W blue
Cylinder Capacity: 6 rounds

Distinguished primarily by caliber, the **Model 17** and **Model 48 K-22 Masterpiece** revolvers offer features to provide a well-placed shot for the small-game hunter. The front sights are serrated ramp style with a 4″ barrel and Patridge style with 6″ and 8″ barrels. Blades are mounted on the ramp base. The rear sight is S&W's micrometer

Smith & Wesson's Model 686 Distinguished Combat Magnum *(above opposite)* has excellent balance for reduced recoil and better sighting. A law enforcer's favorite is the very accurate Smith & Wesson Model 459 9mm Semiautomatic Pistol *(opposite)*. The Model 669 9mm Semi-Automatic Pistol *(above)* comes with two 12-round magazines, and a 20-round magazine is available from the company. Most S&W automatics incorporate trigger-pull cocking double action, including the .45 ACP Model 645 Semi-Automatic *(at left)*.

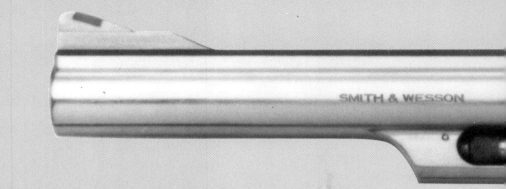

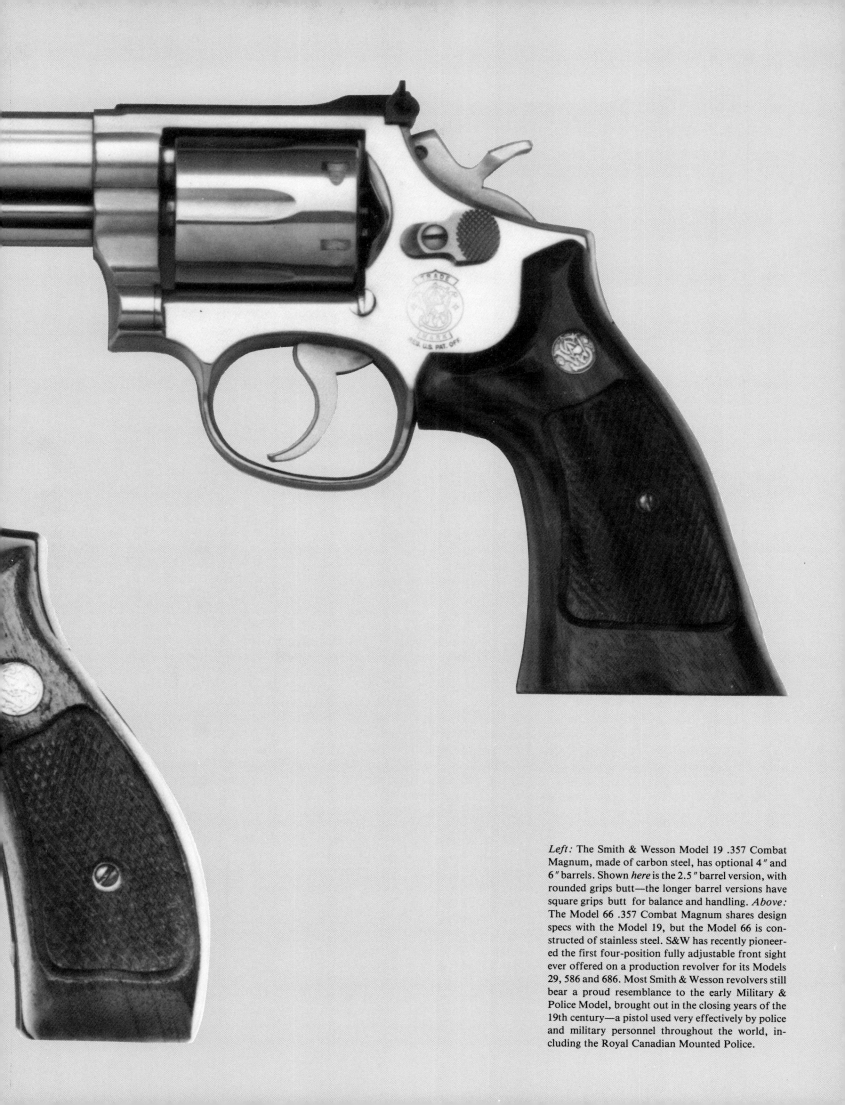

Left: The Smith & Wesson Model 19 .357 Combat Magnum, made of carbon steel, has optional 4″ and 6″ barrels. Shown *here* is the 2.5″ barrel version, with rounded grips butt—the longer barrel versions have square grips butt for balance and handling. *Above:* The Model 66 .357 Combat Magnum shares design specs with the Model 19, but the Model 66 is constructed of stainless steel. S&W has recently pioneered the first four-position fully adjustable front sight ever offered on a production revolver for its Models 29, 586 and 686. Most Smith & Wesson revolvers still bear a proud resemblance to the early Military & Police Model, brought out in the closing years of the 19th century—a pistol used very effectively by police and military personnel throughout the world, including the Royal Canadian Mounted Police.

click sight, adjustable for both windage and elevation. Both models have square butts and monogramed, checkered walnut stocks.

Smith & Wesson Model 19/66 Combat Magnum Revolvers

Type: K frame, double action
Caliber: .357 Magnum, .38 S&W Special
Barrel Length: 2.5", 4", 6"
Weight: 30.5 oz to 39 oz
Length: 7.5" to 11.38" overall
Finish: S&W bright blue or nickel (Model 19); satin (Model 66)
Cylinder Capacity: 6 rounds

Smith & Wesson's **Combat Magnums** come in the **Model 19**, constructed of carbon steel, and the **Model 66** constructed of stainless steel. Both models sport monogramed, checkered Goncalo Alves target stocks with speed loader cut stocks on the 4" and 6" barrel versions. The 2.5" barrel guns have round butt service stocks.

Model 66 sights are a red ramp on ramp base front and the S&W micrometer click sight, rear. Model 19 offers the same front sight style with all three barrel lengths or a serrated ramp with 2.5" and 4" barrels and a Patridge style front sight with the 6" barrel. Its rear sight is the S&W micrometer click sight and is available with a white outline red ramp. Hammers and triggers on both Models 19 and 66 vary based on corresponding barrel length.

Medium 'L' Frame Revolvers: Smith & Wesson Model 581/681 Distinguished Service Magnums

Type: L frame, double action
Caliber: .357 Magnum, .38 SW Special
Barrel Length: 4"
Weight: 38 oz
Length: 9.38" overall
Finish: S&W blue or nickel (Model 581), satin (Model 681)
Cylinder Capacity: 6 rounds

Smith & Wesson's **Distinguised Service Revolvers** are available in the carbon steel **Model 581** and the stainless steel **Model 681**. Both versions have a serrated ramp front sight and a fixed square notch rear sight. Grips are checkered walnut with the S&W monogram.

Smith & Wesson Model 586/686 Distinguished Combat Revolvers

Type: L frame, double action
Caliber: .357 Magnum, .38 S&W Special
Barrel Length: 4", 6", 8.38"
Weight: 41 oz to 53 oz
Length: 9.56" to 13.81" overall
Finish: S&W Bright blue or nickel (Model 586); satin (Model 686)
Cylinder Capacity: 6 rounds

Distinguished Combat Revolvers from Smith & Wesson are available in the carbon steel **Model 586** and the stainless steel **Model 686**. Known for their beefed-up cylinder wall, barrel throat and top strap, these L frame revolvers were designed specifically to accomodate the powerful .357 Magnum round. The heavy-barreled L frame with full length extractor shroud gives excellent balance for reduced recoil and better recovery. Both models have a S&W red ramp on ramp base front sight with a four position positive click adjustable sight available on 6" and 8.38" barrel lengths. The rear sight is S&W's micrometer click sight, adjustable for windage and elevation. Grips for both models are the monogramed checkered Goncalo Alves target stocks with speed loader cut.

Smith & Wesson Large 'N' Frame Revolvers: Smith & Wesson Model 25 Revolver

Type: N frame, double action
Caliber: .45 Colt
Barrel Length: 4", 6", 8.38"
Weight: 44 oz to 50 oz
Length: 9.56" to 13.88" overall
Finish: S&W bright blue or nickel
Cylinder Capacity: 6 rounds

Smith & Wesson's .45 Colt revolver is constructed of carbon steel with monogramed, checkered Goncalo Alves target grips. It features a .500" target hammer and .400" serrated target trigger, front red ramp on ramp base sight, and a S&W rear sight adjustable for windage and elevation.

Smith & Wesson Model 27 .357 Magnum Revolver

Type: N frame, double action
Caliber: .357 Magnum, .38 S&W Special
Barrel Length: 4", 6", 8.38"
Weight: 44 oz to 49 oz
Length: 9.56" to 11.81" overall
Finish: S&W bright blue or nickel
Cylinder Capacity: 6 rounds

The oldest **N-Frame** Magnum still in production by S&W, this sturdy revolver has been a favorite of handgunners since first presented to J Edgar Hoover in 1935. Designed to absorb the energy of high-velocity hunting loads, the **Model 27** .357 Magnum is constructed of carbon steel and has a .400" serrated target trigger, .500" target hammer, and a finely checkered top strap and barrel rib. The front sight is a S&W red ramp for the 4" barrel and Patridge style for 6" and 8.38" barrels. The rear sight is the S&W micrometer click sight adjustable for windage and elevation.

Smith & Wesson Model 28 Highway Patrolman Revolver

Type: N frame, double action
Caliber: .357 Magnum, .38 S&W Special
Barrel Length: 4" and 6"
Weight: 41 oz and 44 oz
Length: 9.31" and 11.06" overall
Finish: S&W satin blue with sandblast stippling on barrel rib
Cylinder Capacity: 6 rounds

The .357 **Highway Patrolman** model is carbon steel available with either monogramed checkered walnut service stocks or walnut target grips. Its hammer is .400" semi-target style and it sports a .265" serrated service trigger. The front sight of this .357 Magnum revolver is a serrated ramp on ramp base; the rear sight is S&W's adjustable micrometer click sight.

The Model 586 Distinguished Combat Revolver *(left)* from Smith & Wesson is available in .357 Magnum and .38 S&W Special, and has optional adjustable front and rear sights. The Smith & Wesson Model 629 .44 Magnum Revolver *(below left)* is made of stainless steel. S&W pioneered the first production Magnum pistols—the .357, .41 and .44 Magnums. The Model 639 9mm Semi-Automatic Pistol *(below right)*, in stainless steel, features an ambidextrous safety.

Smith & Wesson Model 29/629 .44 Magnums

Type: N frame, double action
Caliber: .44 Magnum, .44 Special
Barrel Length: 4″, 6″, 8.38″ (Model 29 also available with 10.63″)
Weight: 44 oz to 57.5 oz (Model 29 with 10.63″ barrel)
Length: 9.63″ to 16.81″ overall
Finish: S&W bright blue or nickel (Model 29); satin (Model 629)
Cylinder Capacity: 6 rounds

The Smith & Wesson .44 Magnum is known to be first rate in strength and accuracy for handgun hunting. Designed for powerful handgun ammunition, the **Model 29** is constructed of carbon steel and the **Model 629**

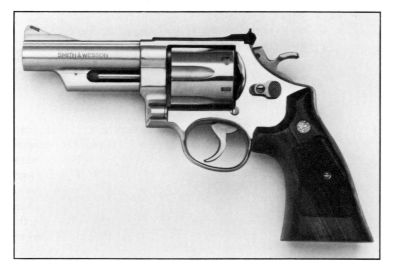

is the same large-framed six-shooter in stainless steel. With its 10.63″ barrel, the Model 29 metallic-silhouette shooter comes equipped with a four-position front sight allowing for a quick change of elevation without altering the fully adjustable rear sight. Both Models 29 and 629 sport S&W monogramed checkered Goncalo Alves target grips.

Smith & Wesson Model 57/657 .41 Magnums

Type: N frame, double action
Caliber: .41 Magnum
Barrel Length: 4″, 6″, 8.38″
Weight: 44.2 oz to 52.5 oz
Length: 9.63″ to 13.98″ overall
Finish: S&W bright blue or nickel (Model 57); satin (Model 657)
Cylinder Capacity: 6 rounds
The two versions of the Smith & Wesson .41 Magnum large frame revolver are distinguished by their sights and materials only. The **Model 57** is made of carbon steel and **Model 657** is made of stainless steel. Both guns feature a .500″ target hammer, .400″ smooth combat trigger, and monogramed checkered Goncalo Alves target grips. Model 57's sights are red ramp on ramp-base front, adjustable micrometer click sight with white outline notch rear. Model 657's sights consist of a serrated black ramp on ramp base in front and a blue adjustable S&W micrometer click sight in rear.

Smith & Wesson Model 624 .44 Target Revolver

Type: N frame, double action
Caliber: .44 S&W Special
Barrel Length: 4″ and 6.5″
Weight: 41.5 oz and 43 oz
Length: 9.5″ to 11.75″ overall
Finish: Satin
Cylinder Capacity: 6 rounds
Smith & Wesson's 1985 Target **Model 624** offers a large frame revolver in .44 caliber

stainless steel. It has a serrated black ramp on ramp base front sight and a rear adjustable S&W micrometer click sight with white outline notch. The hammer varies from .400″ semi-target to .500″ target style depending on barrel length as does the trigger style vary from .312″ smooth combat (with a 4″ barrel) to .400″ serrated target (with the 6.5″ barrel).

Smith & Wesson 9mm Semi-Automatic Pistols:
Smith & Wesson Model 439/639 Semi-Automatic Pistols

Type: Double action, semi-automatic
Caliber: 9mm Par Luger
Barrel Length: 4″
Weight: 30 oz (Model 439); 36 oz (Model 639)
Length: 7.63″ overall
Finish: S&W blue or nickel (Model 439); satin (Model 639)
Magazine Capacity: 8 rounds
Smith & Wesson's two 9mm, 8-shot, semi-automatic pistols have an ambidextrous safety and monogramed, checkered walnut grips. The lightweight **Model 439** has an aluminum alloy frame and **Model 639** is constructed of stainless steel. Both pistols have a serrated ramp front sight and are available with either a fixed rear sight or S&W's adjustable sight with micrometer click.

Smith & Wesson Model 459/659 9mm Semi-Automatic Pistols

Type: Double action, semi-automatic
Caliber: 9mm Par Luger
Barrel Length: 4″
Weight: 30 oz (Model 459); 39.5 oz (Model 659)
Length: 7.63″ overall
Finish: S&W blue or nickel (Model 459); satin (Model 659)
Magazine Capacity: 14 rounds
These 14-shot semi-automatics have grips made of checkered, high-impact molded nylon. Available in the aluminum alloy **Model 459** and the stainless steel **Model 659**, the S&W 9mm autoloaders have a three safety system that includes an ambidextrous manual safety, automatic internal firing pin safety, and an automatic magazine interlock which prevents functioning of the hammer or trigger when no magazine is inserted. Both the 459 and 659 also feature a serrated ramp front sight and a choice of a fixed rear sight or S&W's adjustable sight with micrometer click.

Smith & Wesson Model 469/669 9mm Semi-Automatic Pistols

Type: Double action, semi-automatic
Caliber: 9mm Par Luger
Barrel Length: 3.5″
Weight: 26 oz
Length: 6.81″ overall
Finish: Non-glare blue (Model 469); Non-glare stainless (Model 669)
Magazine Capacity: 12 rounds

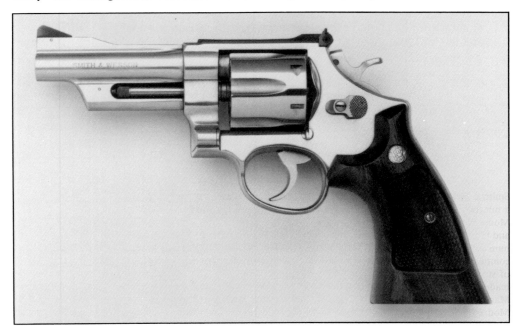

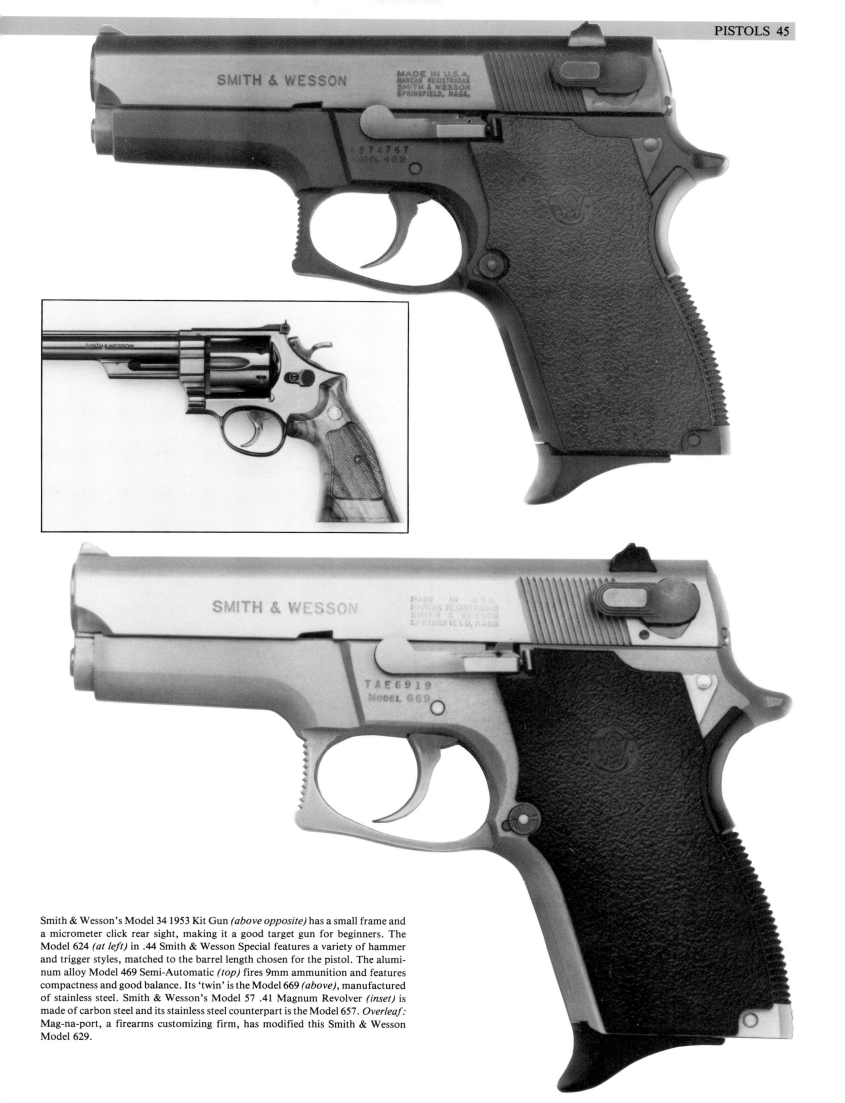

Smith & Wesson's Model 34 1953 Kit Gun *(above opposite)* has a small frame and a micrometer click rear sight, making it a good target gun for beginners. The Model 624 *(at left)* in .44 Smith & Wesson Special features a variety of hammer and trigger styles, matched to the barrel length chosen for the pistol. The aluminum alloy Model 469 Semi-Automatic *(top)* fires 9mm ammunition and features compactness and good balance. Its 'twin' is the Model 669 *(above)*, manufactured of stainless steel. Smith & Wesson's Model 57 .41 Magnum Revolver *(inset)* is made of carbon steel and its stainless steel counterpart is the Model 657. *Overleaf:* Mag-na-port, a firearms customizing firm, has modified this Smith & Wesson Model 629.

SMITH & WESSON

MADE IN U.S.A
MARCAS REGISTRADAS
SMITH & WESSON
SPRINGFIELD, MASS.

A 883239
Model 645

This high-capacity, compact 9mm features a sleek fit, balance, and accuracy in its **Model 469** aluminum alloy and **Model 669** stainless steel versions. Both pistols have a bobbed hammer and rounded rear sight corners, bevelled 12-round magazine well, checkered recurved trigger guard, and S&W's fixed barrel bushing. The overall design makes them especially suited for duty and plain-clothes law enforcement.

Smith & Wesson Model 645 .45 ACP Semi-Automatic Pistol

Type: Double action, semi-automatic
Caliber: .45 ACP
Barrel Length: 5″
Weight: 37.5 oz
Length: 8.63″ overall
Finish: Satin
Magazine Capacity: 8 rounds

Smith & Wesson's .45 ACP semi-automatic has as standard features its stainless steel construction, ball-end barrel, fixed barrel bushing, and grips of checkered, high-impact molded nylon. The front sight is a red ramp on ramp-base and the rear sight is fixed with a white outline, adjustable for windage only.

Smith & Wesson Model 41 .22 Single Action Target Pistol

Type: Single action, semi-automatic
Caliber: .22 LR
Barrel Length: 5.5″ heavy barrel and 7″
Weight: 44 oz (5.5″ heavy barrel); 41 oz (7″ barrel)

Upper opposite: Among customized versions of Smith & Wesson pistols, this ASP conversion of a Smith & Wesson 'hammerless' shows modifications made for utility and convenience, such as the 'see-through magazine' pistol grips, cowl sights atop the receiver and some obvious streamlining. Boasting 'the broadest handgun line in the world,' Smith & Wesson has contributed many, many models to the genre of autoloading pistols. Shown *opposite* is the Smith & Wesson Model 52 .38 Master Semi-Automatic Pistol. This pistol is chambered for .38 Smith & Wesson Special mid-range wadcutter bullets, and is single action, which facilitates the target shooter's

concentration as he systematically cocks and fires his pistol, setting up the 'semi-automatic' action which follows the initial cock-and-fire. The Model 52 comes with two five-round magazines, micrometer click rear sight and partridge ramp front sight. The Smith & Wesson Model 645 Semi-Automatic Pistol *(above)* fires the .45 ACP, a cartridge which is ubiquitous in the world of semi-automatic pistols. Equipped with ramp front and fixed rear sights, made of stainless steel and featuring the high level of craftsmanship with which Smith & Wesson manufactures its firearms, the Model 645 is any shooter's 'safe bet.' Smith & Wesson also offers high-quality custom engraving.

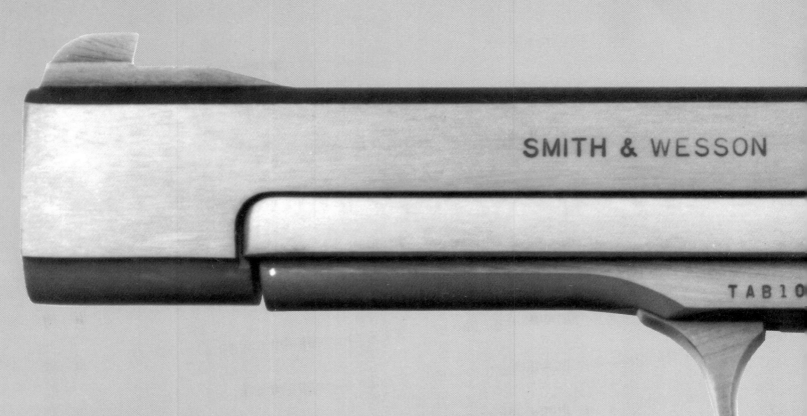

Smith & Wesson's Model 41 Single Action Semi-Automatic Target Pistol *(above and below)* is a single action pistol, built extra-heavy for sighting stability. The receiver 'overhangs' the shooter's thumb, both to aid balancing the 5.5″ heavy barrel *(above)* or 7″ *(below)* barrel, and to promote the pistol's fitting snugly to the shooter's hand. Its .22 Long Rifle cartridges develop sufficient velocity to provide moderate-range target shooting accuracy, and lack the unsettling recoil that many high velocity cartridges produce. At 41 to 44 oz, depending on barrel length, and with a windage and elevation adjustable micrometer click rear sight, the Smith & Wesson Model 41 promises to be a very comfortable and accurate target pistol. Its grips are made of walnut, with checkering and modified right- or left-handed adaptable thumb rest.

Above: The Smith & Wesson Combat Masterpiece is a 6-shot revolver chambered for .38 Smith & Wesson Special—a cartridge which has seen much service with police departments throughout the United States. The thumb toggle just below the hammer is the cylinder catch—one push of this release and the pistol's cylinder hinges down and outward for speedy reloading. Just snap the cylinder into place again and the pistol is ready for more shooting. The Combat Masterpiece is available with a number of barrel lengths—8.38″ *(bottom),* 6″ *(below middle),* 4″ *(below right)* and 2″ *(below left). Opposite:* A USAF sentry stands alert with his guard dog and (its square butt sticking out from his hip) his Smith & Wesson .38 caliber Model 15.

Length: 9.06″ (with 5.5″ barrel); 10.5″ (with 7″ barrel)
Finish: S&W bright blue
Magazine Capacity: 10 rounds
With a choice of a 5.5″ heavy barrel and standard 7″ barrel, Smith & Wesson's .22 caliber single shot semi-automatic features a concealed hammer, .365″ width trigger with S&W grooving and adjustable trigger stop, and checkered walnut grips with a modified thumb rest that adapts to right and left hand shooters alike. The front sight is Patridge undercut, and in the rear is the adjustable S&W micrometer click sight.

Smith & Wesson Model 52 .38 Master Single Action Target Pistol
Type: Single action, semi-automatic
Caliber: .38 S&W Special, Mid Range Wadcutter
Barrel Length: 5″
Weight: 40.5 oz
Length: 8.88″ overall
Finish: S&W bright blue
Magazine Capacity: 5 rounds
Smith & Wesson's **Model 52** semi-automatic pistol is made of carbon steel and sports checkered walnut, monogramed grips. The front sight is Patridge style on a ramp base and the rear sight is the S&W micrometer click sight with a wide (.88″) sight slide. This model also features a .365″ width trigger with S&W grooving and adjustable trigger stop.

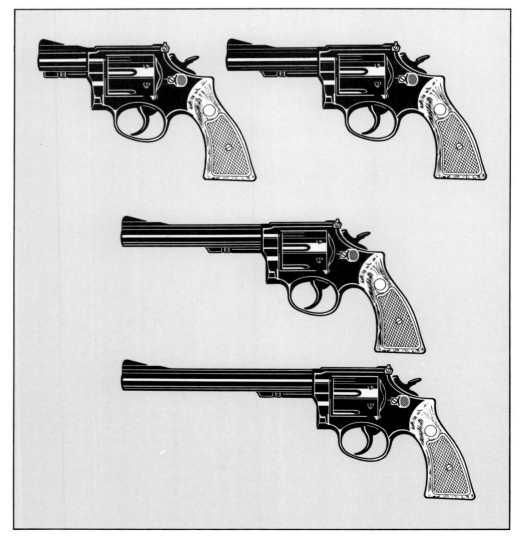

Springfield Armory, Inc

1911-A1

Caliber: .45 ACP or 9mm Parabellum
Barrel Length: 5.04″ Standard; 3.63″
    Officers
Weight: 35.62 oz Standard; 34 oz Officers
Length: 8.59″ overall Standard; 7.25″
    overall Officers

Finish: Military parkerized or optional
    blued finish
Magazine Capacity: Standard .45: 7 in
    mag, 1 in chamber
Standard 9mm: 8 in mag, 1 in chamber
Officers .45: 6 in mag, 1 in chamber
Officers 9mm: 7 in mag, 1 in chamber
A faithful copy of the original government
model, the **1911-A1** comes in three varia-

tions: the Standard Military, Officers, and
Custom models. Major component parts are
of forged steel, and the ejection port factory
lowered for reliable feeding and ejection. All
parts are completely interchangeable allowing the Custom model to be built to individual specifications using the Standard
1911-A1 as a base. Factory-assembled match
grade custom pistols are to be added to the
line.

Steel City Arms, Inc

Steel City Arms .22/.25 Pistols

Type: Double action, autoloading
Caliber: .22 LR and .25 ACP
Barrel Length: 2.5″
Weight: 18 oz
Length: 5.5″ overall
Finish: Matte
Magazine Capacity: 6 rounds
Steel City's **'Double Deuce'** (.22) and **'Two
Bit Special'** (.25) handguns are constructed
of stainless steel with rosewood grips. Both
versions have a slide and frame machined on
a computerized, numerically controlled, ver-
tical milling center for a perfect fit and they
are engraved with a high-tech lazer. They
have fixed sights and an ambidextrous thumb
release safety.

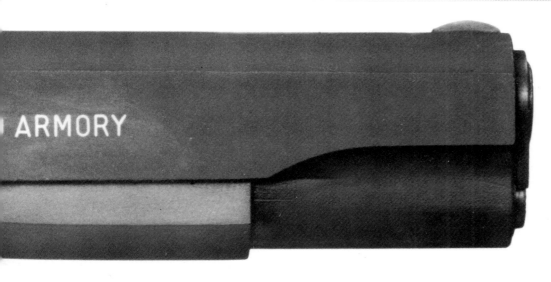

Springfield Armory, Inc, has a long history as armorers to the US military. From the 18th century forward, Springfield has consistently produced some of our finest military arms. *At left* is yet another example of Springfield's reliable expertise. The nearly apocryphal 1911-A1 semi-automatic pistol, chambered for the .45 ACP cartridge, is a weapon that is not exactly meant for target shooting, but is truly a combat arm—it has plenty of knockdown power, and can empty its clip in a hurry. Springfield makes their 1911-A1 in 2 calibers—.45 ACP or 9mm Parabellum, and in 3 versions—any one of which is parts-interchangeable with the Standard 1911-A1 model; also, Springfield's Custom model can be built to individual specs using the Standard 1911-A1 as a base. Steel City Arms' Double Deuce *(below)* in .22 caliber is produced in a high-tech assembly shop to exacting specifications. It features rosewood grips, fixed sights and an ambidextrous thumb-release safety.

Steel City Arms 9mm Pistol

Type: Double-action, autoloading
Caliber: 9mm Parabellum
Barrel Length: 3″ and 6″
Finish: Matte
Magazine Capacity: 12 rounds

A compact, stainless steel pistol from Steel City Arms, the 9mm **'War Eagle'** has rosewood grips, fixed and adjustable sights and and ambidextrous thumb release safety.

Sturm, Ruger & Company, Inc

Ruger Bisley Single Action Revolver

Type: Single action
Caliber: .22 LR, .32 Mag (standard model), .357 Mag, .41 Mag, .44 Mag, .45 Colt (large frame model)
Barrel Length: 6.5″ to 7.5″ (large frame model)
Weight: 41 oz to 48 oz (large frame)
Length: 11.5″ to 13″ overall
Finish: Satin polished and blued
Cylinder Capacity: 6 shot

The **Bisley** revolver is based on the famous Single-Six design and incorporates a popular 'flattop' frame, cylinders and working components. Its longer grip frames have been designed with a distinctive hand-filling shape with rear screws hidden beneath the

The Ruger GP-100 Double Action Revolver *(above)* combines tried and tested Ruger design with various improvements to make this one of the best-handling Magnums available. Its full-length ejector shroud gives this firearm a muzzle-heavy balance, which helps to stabilize the .357 Magnum's muzzle-lifting recoil. The front sight is easily interchanged with alternate sights of various styles; the rear sight is adjustable for windage and elevation. The Ruger GP-100 handles all .357 Magnum loads, and is also available chambered for .38 Special. Also featured on this model are rubber or wood optional grip panels, anatomically designed for maximum comfort and durability.

This is a Ruger GP-100, field stripped to show its components. *Left to right:* cylinder assembly; main frame; trigger assembly showing transfer bar *(left)*, cylinder pawl *(middle),* and trigger spur; hammer assembly including spring arm; and grip. The GP-100 can be field-stripped in seconds, without special tools.

This Ruger Super Blackhawk .44 Magnum *(at right)* is set up for big game hunting, with its telescopic sight 7.5″ barrel and 'brush country' sling swivels. A customizer, the Mag-na-port company specializes in endowing various manufacturers' Magnum pistols with such features as the vent which is visible on top of this Super Blackhawk's muzzle *(below),* which is one of 2 gas vents, or 'compensators,' which serve to keep the muzzle down by letting gas escape upward during recoil—for better accuracy; and they rid the bullet's path of the turbulence normally caused by excess gas build up.

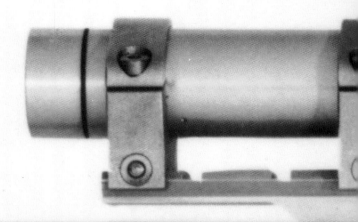

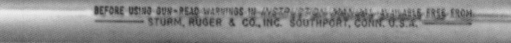

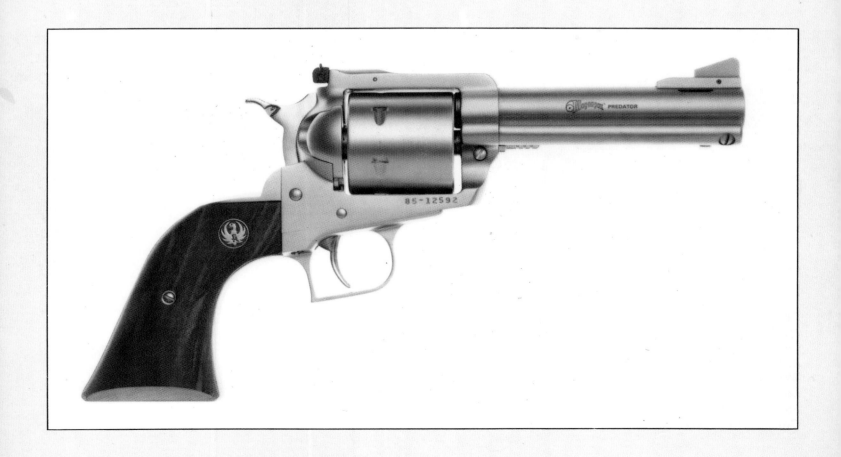

Goncalo Alves grip panels. The standard .22 LR and .32 Mag models are suited for informal target shooting and small game and varmint hunting.

The large frame Bisley revolver adds 1" to barrel and overall length. All four caliber models sport adjustable sights with other features as per the standard Bisley revolver. Both versions of this target shooting gun are available with either fluted or unfluted cylinders that are roll marked in a classic styling reminiscent of the 1890 Bisley, England era.

Ruger GP-100 Double Action Revolver
Type: Double action
Caliber: .357 Magnum, .38 Special
Barrel Length: 4"
Weight: 41 oz
Length: 9.38" overall
Finish: Blued
Cylinder Capacity: 6 rounds

Designed for unlimited use of .357 Magnum ammunition, the **GP-100** incorporates a wider frame that has been increased in critical areas which support the barrel and solid frame side walls that provide strength and rigidity. The lock mechanism is contained within the trigger guard which is inserted into the frame as a single subassembly. Anatomically designed to fit the hands of a majority of shooters, Ruger cushioned grip panels are an added feature.

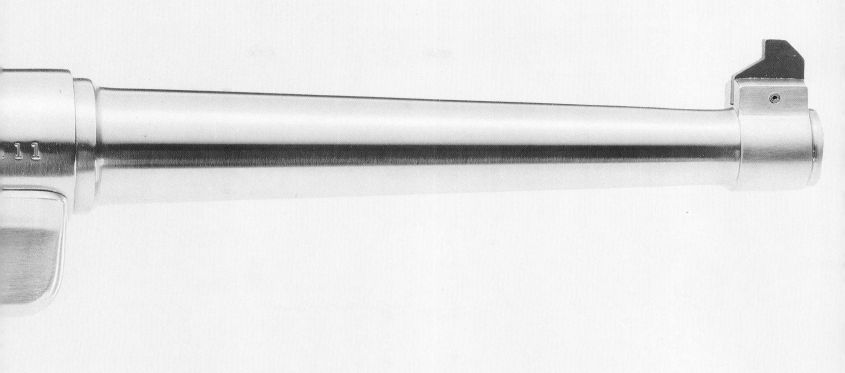

Shown *here* is the Ruger Mark II Standard model. Refinements made on this second generation version of the famous Ruger .22 Long Rifle autoloader include a 10-shot magazine, a safety that permits bolt actuation while the safety is 'on' and a bolt stop which holds the bolt open when the pistol's last round has been fired. The Mark II Standard model's rear sight is a square notch type, dovetail mounted, is adjustable for windage and works well with the wide-blade Partridge style front sight.

Other special features of the GP-100 include the long ejector shroud which helps to achieve the slight muzzle-heavy balance considered desirable for a steady hold and barrels constructed with a wide top rib, serrated to present a glare-free surface. The standard Ruger GP-100 is fitted with a 4″ heavy barrel but is also available with a 6″ barrel.

Ruger Mark II Automatic Pistols

Type: Automatic rimfire
Caliber: .22 LR
Barrel Length: 4.75″ to 10″ (Bull Barrel Model)
Weight: 2.25 lbs to 3.25 lbs

Length: 8.31″ to 14″ overall (Bull Barrel Model)
Finish: Blued or satin (stainless steel models)
Magazine Capacity: 10 rounds

The features of the **Ruger Mark II** automatics are basically those refinements made to the original **Ruger Standard** and **Mark I Target** model pistols, over one million of which have been produced since 1949. The Mark II design includes a bolt stop to hold the bolt open after the last shot and after a loaded magazine is inserted; a bolt stop thumb piece to provide for manual activation of the bolt stop at any time; an improved trigger and trigger pivot retainer; a modified

safety; a 10-shot magazine that provides trouble-free feeding and smoother insertion/ withdrawal of the magazine.

The **Mark II Standard** model is available in either black gloss or stainless steel with medium weight barrels of 4.75″ and 6″. Its front sight is a fixed Patridge type and the rear sight is square notch, dovetail mounted, ajustable for windage. The **Mark II Target** model has a 6.88″ tapered and button rifled barrel that provides an added refinement for competitive target shooting. Its front sight is the Patridge type front blade, .125″ wide and undercut to prevent glare. The rear sight has click adjustments for windage and elevation.

The **Mark II Bull Barrel** model is identical to the Target Model except that it is equipped with a heavier Bull barrel in two lengths, 5.5″ and 10″. This barrel configuration was developed to meet the needs of those shooters who prefer a greater concentration of

Two views of a Ruger Bisley Single-Action Revolver *(top of page):* Patterned after the British 'flat top' target pistol, the Ruger Bisley is available in 2 frame sizes to handle many light and heavy calibers. *At left* are 2 variations of the Ruger Mark II pistol. *Left to right*—the 'Bull Barrel Model,' designed for shooters preferring muzzle-heavy balance, and the Mark II Target Model.

Mag cartridge, offers a 7.5" and a 10.5" barreled version that is a favorite with hunters and silhouette shooters. Available in both blued finish and stainless steel, the Super Blackhawk revolver has a wide, deeply serrated hammer spur and Dragoon style grip frame.

weight at the muzzle. Both the Target and Bull Barrel Models are also available in stainless steel.

Ruger New Model Blackhawk Revolvers
Type: Single action
Caliber: .30 Carbine, .38 Special, .357 Mag, .41 Mag, .45 Long Colt (Blackhawk); .44 Mag (Super Blackhawk)
Barrel Length: 4.63" to 10.5" (Super Blackhawk)
Weight: 38 oz to 51 oz
Length: 10.25" to 16.38" overall
Cylinder Capacity: 6 rounds

The **New Model Blackhawk Revolver** is engineered for use with powerful modern centerfire cartridges. Incorporated into this massive 38-to-44 oz gun is the patented Ruger transfer-bar ignition mechanism which all but prevents the possibility of accidental discharge.

The **Super Blackhawk**, designed and constructed to take advantage of the powerful .44

Ruger New Model Single-Six Revolvers
Type: Single-action
Caliber: .22 LR (Super model) and .32 H&R Mag
Barrel Length: 4.63" to 9.5" overall
Weight: 31 oz to 38 oz
Length: 9.88" to 14.88" overall
Finish: Blued or satin (stainless models)
Cylinder Capacity: 6 rounds

The Ruger **Single-Six Revolver** was introduced over 30 years ago and is one of the most popular single actions ever made. 'New Model' refinements were made in 1973 and

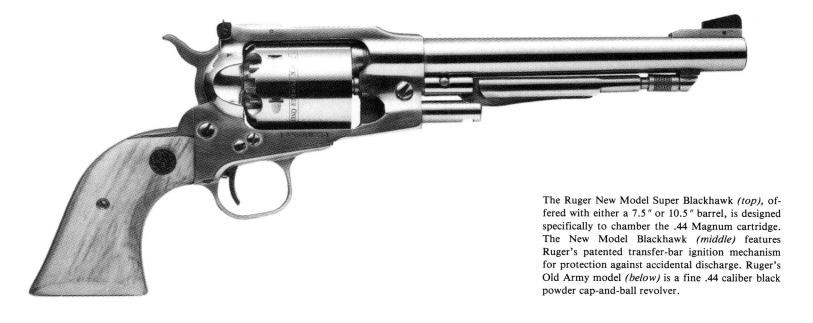

The Ruger New Model Super Blackhawk *(top)*, offered with either a 7.5" or 10.5" barrel, is designed specifically to chamber the .44 Magnum cartridge. The New Model Blackhawk *(middle)* features Ruger's patented transfer-bar ignition mechanism for protection against accidental discharge. Ruger's Old Army model *(below)* is a fine .44 caliber black powder cap-and-ball revolver.

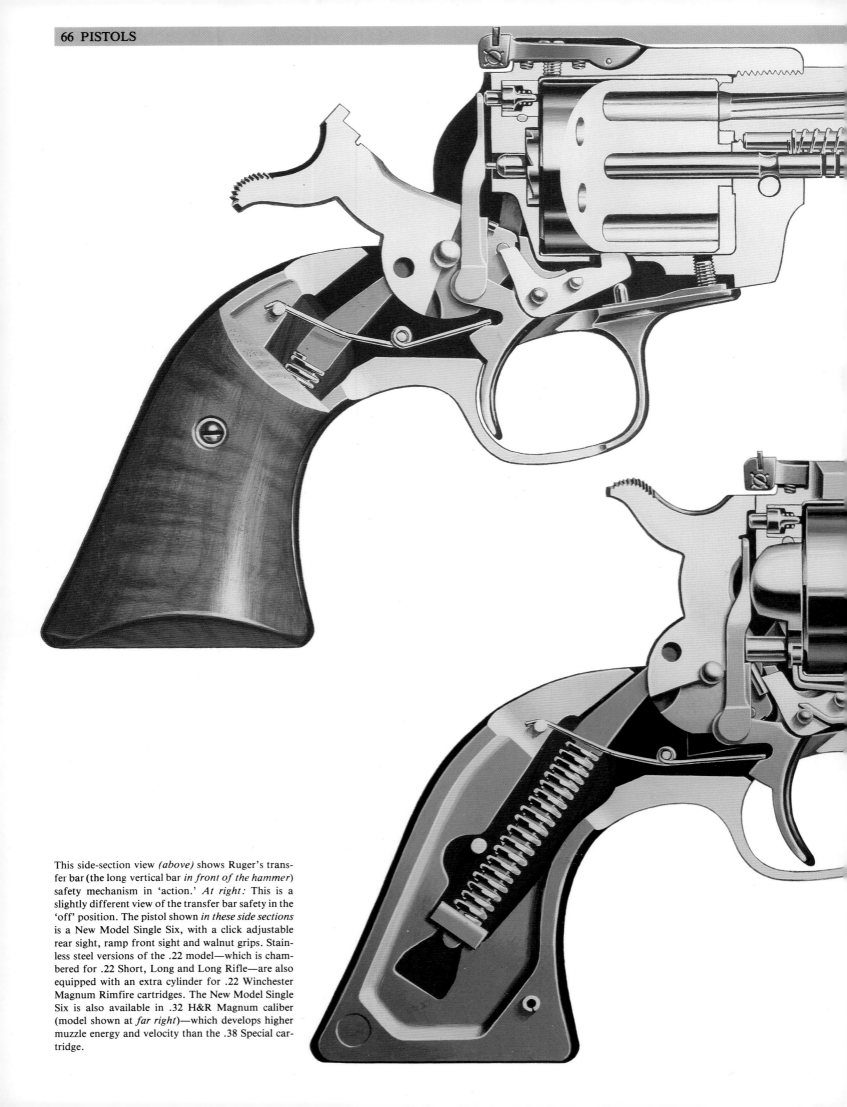

This side-section view *(above)* shows Ruger's transfer bar (the long vertical bar *in front of the hammer*) safety mechanism in 'action.' *At right:* This is a slightly different view of the transfer bar safety in the 'off' position. The pistol shown *in these side sections* is a New Model Single Six, with a click adjustable rear sight, ramp front sight and walnut grips. Stainless steel versions of the .22 model—which is chambered for .22 Short, Long and Long Rifle—are also equipped with an extra cylinder for .22 Winchester Magnum Rimfire cartridges. The New Model Single Six is also available in .32 H&R Magnum caliber (model shown at *far right*)—which develops higher muzzle energy and velocity than the .38 Special cartridge.

led to today's Single-Six and **Super Single-Six** models. Both contemporary versions sport Goncalo Alves or walnut grip panels, a Patridge type ramp front sight and a rear sight click adjustable for windage and elevation.

The .22 LR caliber **New Model Super Single-Six** is available in hardened chome-moly alloy steel or with components of stainless steel. The .32 Mag **New Model Single-Six Revolver** (in chrome-moly alloy steel only) is designed for small game, varmint, and target shooting and will handle .32 S&W and .32 S&W Long cartridges as well.

Ruger Old Army Cap and Ball Revolver
Type: Single action
Caliber: .44 black powder
Barrel Length: 7.5″
Weight: 46 oz
Finish: Blued or satin (stainless steel model)

The Ruger black powder **Old Army** revolver has been designed and engineered to in-

corporate the best mechanical features and modern materials with the beautiful lines of the classic cap and ball models. It has a .443″ bore, .451″ groove and is designed for .457″ diameter pure lead ball or conical bullets. The sights are ramp front and target rear, adjustable for windage and elevation.

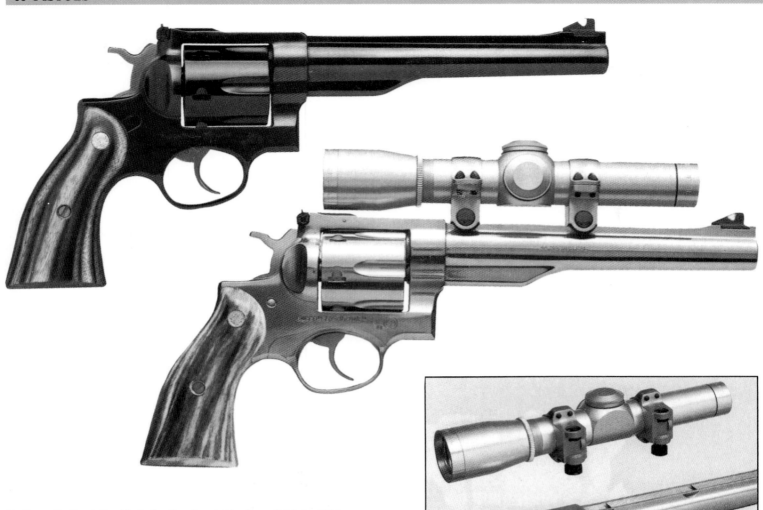

The Ruger Redhawk Double Action Revolver *(at top)* is available in .41 Magnum and .44 Magnum calibers. The Redhawk shown *above* has adjustable front and rear sights as well as the Ruger Redhawk integral scope mounting system *(at right)*. Ruger's Service-Six Double-Action Revolver *(bottom of page)* features Ruger's transfer-bar safety system, and is available chambered for .357 Magnum and .38 Special cartridges. Ruger's Speed-Six *(below)* is basically the same as the Service-Six, but has a rounded-butt style frame for compactness.

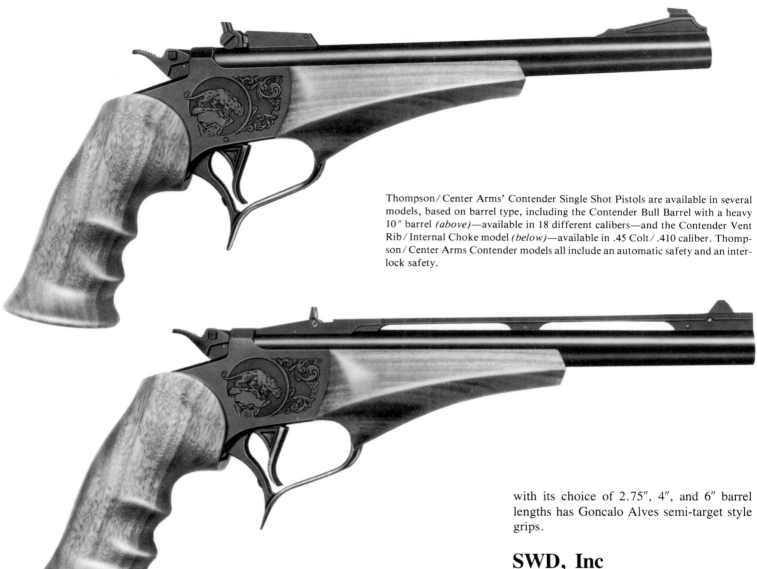

Thompson/Center Arms' Contender Single Shot Pistols are available in several models, based on barrel type, including the Contender Bull Barrel with a heavy 10″ barrel *(above)*—available in 18 different calibers—and the Contender Vent Rib/Internal Choke model *(below)*—available in .45 Colt/.410 caliber. Thompson/Center Arms Contender models all include an automatic safety and an interlock safety.

Ruger Redhawk Double-Action Revolvers

Type: Double action
Caliber: .41 Mag, .44 Mag
Barrel Length: 5.5″ and 7.5″
Weight: 52 oz
Length: 11″ and 13″ overall
Finish: Blued and satin (stainless steel)
Cylinder Capacity: 6 rounds
Available in both stainless steel and alloy steel models, the Ruger **Redhawk** is the first double action revolver designed to withstand the stresses of the potent .44 Magnum cartridge. Its solid side-wall frame eliminates the need for a removable sideplate and contributes to the gun's overall strength. Its grip frame is contoured to provide full Magnum-style grip for comfort and security. The Redhawk has a barrel forged with an integral rib and ejector housing and a front sight system that features interchangeable front sights.

Ruger Service-Six Double-Action Revolvers

Type: Double action
Caliber: .357 Magnum, .38 Special
Barrel Length: 2.75″, 4″, and 6″
(Security-Six Model)
Weight: 34 oz (with 4″ barrel)
Length: 9.25″ overall (with 4″ barrel)
Finish: Blued and satin (stainless steel)
Cylinder Capacity: 6 rounds
The Ruger **Service-Six Revolver** is available in either heat treated chrome-moly steel or stainless steel alloys. Its barrel, sighting rib, and ejector rod housing are an integral unit and it field strips in seconds without the use of tools. Its internal safety system utilizes a transfer-bar to prevent discharge unless the trigger is held to the rear. The compact **Speed-Six Revolver** is the same basic design as its Service-Six counterpart and features a round butt style frame for compactness and carrying comfort.
Whereas the sights of the Service-Six and Speed-Six Models are fixed, the **Security-Six Double-Action Revolver** has a rear sight adjustable for windage and elevation and a serrated front sight. The **Security Model**

with its choice of 2.75″, 4″, and 6″ barrel lengths has Goncalo Alves semi-target style grips.

SWD, Inc

Cobray M-11/9mm Semi-automatic Pistol

Type: Straight blowback, semi-automatic
Caliber: 9mm Par
Barrel Length: 5.25″
Weight: 3.25 lbs
Length: 11.25″ overall
Magazine Capacity: 32 rounds
SWD's **Cobray** semi-automatic is a compact, lightweight pistol designed for sustained target use. It has a front protected post sight, manually operated safety lever, and is magazine fed. The front end of the barrel is threaded to accept a barrel extension and various other accessories.

Thompson/Center Arms

Contender Single Shot Pistols

Caliber: 21 calibers ranging from .22 LR to .44 Magnum
Barrel Length: 10″ and 14″
Weight: 43 oz with 10″ barrel; 56 oz with 14″ bull barrel
Length: 13.5″ overall (10″ barrel); 17.5″ overall (14″ barrel)
Finish: Blued or satin (Armour Alloy II models)

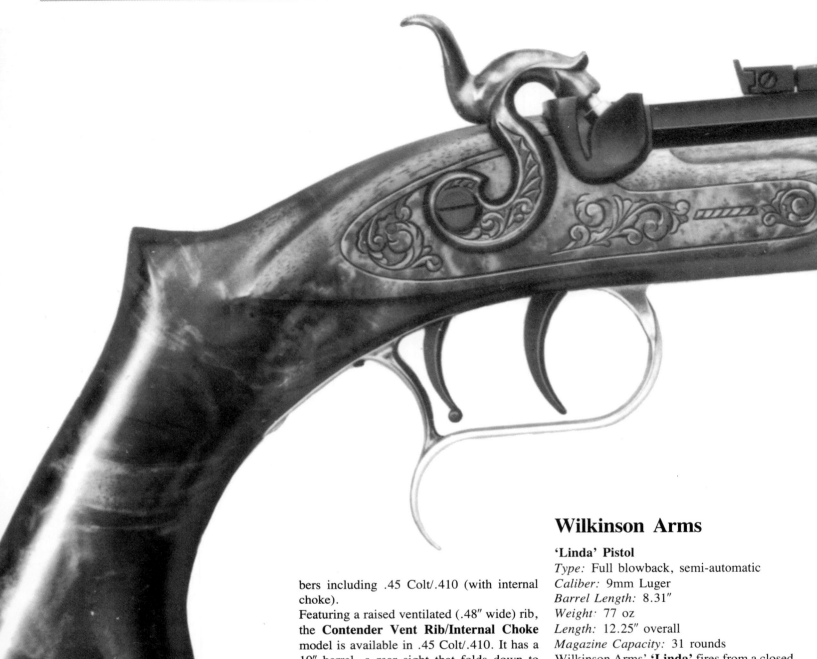

The **Contender** series of pistols all employ a single shot, break open design. Various barrel styles are offered in either blue or Armour Alloy II finishes and triggers are the grooved, wide target type. The automatic safety stays in a safety position until the trigger is pulled for firing and an interlock prevents the pistol from firing if the barrel is not completely closed and locked.

The **Contender Octagon Barrel** model with its 10″ barrel is the trimmest and lightest in weight of the four Contender models. It is available in .22 LR and .22 Win Mag calibers only. Iron sights are fully adjustable Patridge style. The **Contender Bull Barrel** model has a 10″ barrel, iron Patridge style sights, and is available in 18 different cali-

bers including .45 Colt/.410 (with internal choke).

Featuring a raised ventilated (.48″ wide) rib, the **Contender Vent Rib/Internal Choke** model is available in .45 Colt/.410. It has a 10″ barrel, a rear sight that folds down to provide an unobstructed sighting plane when shot cartridges are being used, and a patented detachable choke. Finally, the **Contender Super '14'** model sports a 14″ bull barrel and is chambered in twelve workhorse calibers. It is equipped with a fully adjustable rear sight and ramp front Patridge style sight.

Patriot Percussion Target Pistol

Type: Single shot, percussion
Caliber: .36 and .45
Barrel Length: 9″
Weight: 36 oz
Stock: American walnut

Thompson/Center's black powder **Percussion Target Pistol** features a hooked breech, double set triggers, adjustable Patridge type target sights, solid brass trim, and dolphin shaped hammer. Constructed from investment castings of modern steel, all working parts are heat treated to insure long life.

Wilkinson Arms

'Linda' Pistol

Type: Full blowback, semi-automatic
Caliber: 9mm Luger
Barrel Length: 8.31″
Weight: 77 oz
Length: 12.25″ overall
Magazine Capacity: 31 rounds

Wilkinson Arms' **'Linda'** fires from a closed breech with a bolt type safety and bolt type magazine catch. This pistol has a timed barrel, ejection port equipped with automatic trap door, and its receiver sports a dovetail scope mount. 'Linda' comes with Williams adjustable sights and a maplewood foregrip.

'Sherry' Pistol

Type: Full blowback, semi-automatic
Caliber: .22 LR
Barrel Length: 2.13″
Weight: 9.25 oz
Length: 4.38″ overall
Magazine Capacity: 8 rounds

'Sherry' features a cross bolt safety and fires from a closed breech. After firing the empty case is ejected and a fresh round is chambered. To fire again, trigger pressure must be released, then pressed again until the last cartridge has been chambered and fired. 'Sherry' is offered in either a blue or blue and gold finish.

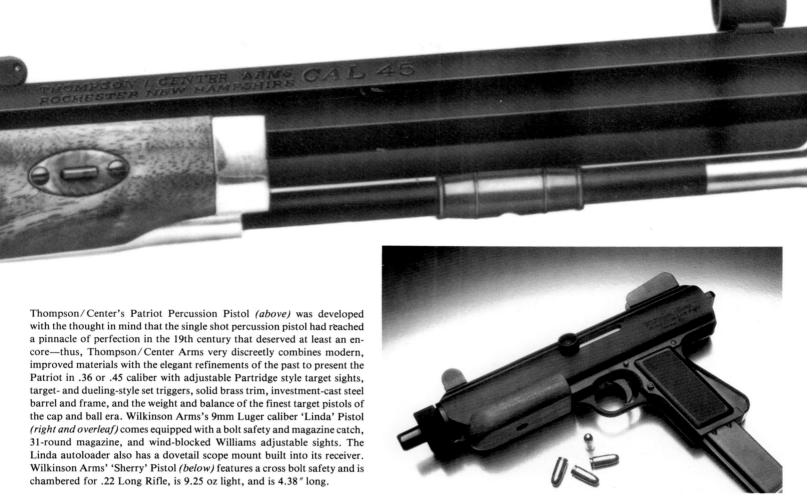

Thompson/Center's Patriot Percussion Pistol *(above)* was developed with the thought in mind that the single shot percussion pistol had reached a pinnacle of perfection in the 19th century that deserved at least an encore—thus, Thompson/Center Arms very discreetly combines modern, improved materials with the elegant refinements of the past to present the Patriot in .36 or .45 caliber with adjustable Partridge style target sights, target- and dueling-style set triggers, solid brass trim, investment-cast steel barrel and frame, and the weight and balance of the finest target pistols of the cap and ball era. Wilkinson Arms's 9mm Luger caliber 'Linda' Pistol *(right and overleaf)* comes equipped with a bolt safety and magazine catch, 31-round magazine, and wind-blocked Williams adjustable sights. The Linda autoloader also has a dovetail scope mount built into its receiver. Wilkinson Arms' 'Sherry' Pistol *(below)* features a cross bolt safety and is chambered for .22 Long Rifle, is 9.25 oz light, and is 4.38″ long.

RIFLES

A-Square Co, Inc

A-Square Rifles
Caliber: 7X57 to .500 mag (Hannibal) or
.450 mag (Caesar)
Weight: 9 to 12.5 lbs based on caliber
and sights
Barrel Length: 22″ to 26″
Stock: Deluxe or fancy walnut
Sights: Open, receiver, or telescopic
A-Square's two models are the **Hannibal,** built on the P-17 Enfield action, and the **Caesar,** built on the Remington M-700 action. Both rifles are designed for hunting and include features to facilitate the probability of its success. Developed by A-Square, the guns' 'Coil-Chek' stock has a greater cross-sectional area of butt and three times the wood normally flanking either side of the magazine well. The added wood reduces flexion and, combined with steel crossbolts, fiberglass bedding, and bedding gaps at receiver tang and trigger guard, reduces recoil and eliminates splitting.

Other hunting features include: outward sweeping bolt handles, smooth cartridge feeding with feed lips and feed ramps to prevent jamming, faster twist rates for bullet stability, and flexible positioning of scope mounts to prevent recoil eye injury.

Bushmaster Firearms

Bushmaster Assault Rifle
Type: Semi-automatic
Caliber: .223
Barrel Length: 18.5″
Weight: 6.25 lbs

Length: 38″ overall
Magazine Capacity: 30 rounds
With either a solid wood or folding stock, the **Bushmaster** combines the successful designs of the M-16 magazine, pistol grip, and the AK's gas system. This compact and reliable pistol grip rifle has a steel alloy upper receiver and one-piece bolt carrier and take-off assemblies.

Champlin Firearms Inc

Champlin Bolt Action Rifle
Type: Bolt action
Caliber: Various
Barrel Length: To 26″
Stock: French walnut
The basic Champlin **Bolt Action Rifle** has either a right- or left-handed action, all steel parts, hand lapped bolt, adjustable trigger, hinged floor plate, shotgun-type tang safety, two-panel bolt knob checkering, and a standard tapered octagonal or round barrel. These rifles can be fitted with an old English recoil pad and a forend option of several different sizes. All other specifications are at the buyer's request.

Chipmunk Manufacturing, Inc

Chipmunk Single Shot Rifle
Type: Single shot bolt action
Caliber: .22 and .22 Magnum
Barrel Length: 16.13″
Weight: 2.5 lbs
Length: 30″ overall
Stock: Walnut
Sights: Rear peep sight adjustable for windage and elevation; front ramp with post
Chipmunk's **Single Shot Rifle** is chambered for .22 Caliber short, long, or long rifle cartridges with standard or high velocity. It is manually cocked with a stainless steel low scope bolt handle and has a 2.5 lb trigger

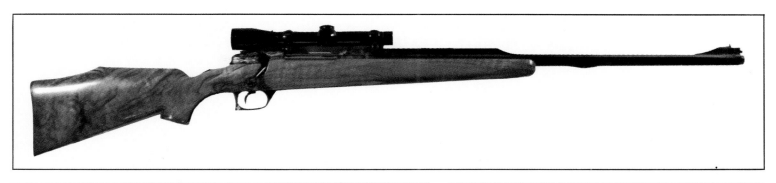

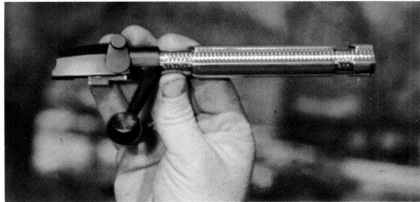

Shown *at top, opposite* is Bushmaster's Combination Weapons System—a quick change choice of receivers and stocks for the Bushmaster Assault Rifle. A-Square's .500 Hannibal Magnum *(immediately above)* is a big-game sporter featuring P-17 Enfield action; open, receiver or telescopic sights; heavy, well-bedded stock; and other features to ensure hunting success and shooting comfort. The Champlin Bolt Action Rifle *(top half of page)* features a very strong and fast bolt action, fully adjustable trigger, choice of right- or left-handed action and a standard tapered octagonal or round barrel.

pull. For optimum safety, the rebounding firing pin is automatically blocked to prevent accidental discharge.

Colt Industries

Colt Model AR-15 Rifle

Type: Semi-automatic
Caliber: .223 Rem and 5.56 mm (H-Bar, Sporter, Carbine); 9mm Carbine
Barrel Length: 16″ and 20″
Weight: 5.8 lbs to 8 lbs
Length: 32″ to 39″ overall
Finish: Military matte
Magazine Capacity: 5 rounds (20 rounds, 9mm Model)

The **AR-15A2 H-Bar** model adds extra target shooting features to this military style rifle. It incorporates a rear sight adjustable for windage and elevation to 800 meters, a full length heavy barrel for greater stiffness, case deflector for left hand shooters, and a new target style nylon sling. The **AR-15A2 Sporter II** model features a forward bolt assist, stronger nylon ribbed handguard, buttstock and pistol grip with a field sight adjustable for windage and a front sight post adjustable for elevation.

Colt's **AR-15A2 Carbine** combines the .223 Rem caliber of the H-Bar and Sporter models with a 16″ barrel and collapsible buttstock. The short, **AR-15 9mm Carbine** has a basic configuration of an M16, collapsible buttstock, and 16″ barrel.

Feather Enterprises

Feather Enterprises AT-22 Semi-automatic Carbine

Type: Semi-automatic
Caliber: 22 LR
Barrel Length: 17″
Weight: 3.25 lbs
Length: 33.75″
Magazine Capacity: 22 rounds

The **AT-22** incorporates many advanced design features, including a folding stock. The acronym 'AT' stands for 'Advanced Technology,' a reference to Feather Enterprises' painstaking care taken in designing this carbine. Accessories available from Feather En-

terprises for the AT-22 include a full length barrel shroud, 'no-gunsmithing' scope mount, padded carrying case, sling and swivels, a winged front sight and more.

Hopkins & Allen Arms

Brush Rifle

Type: Muzzleloading long gun
Caliber: .36 or .45
Barrel Length: 25″
Weight: 6.5 lbs (.45 Cal model)
Length: 40″ overall

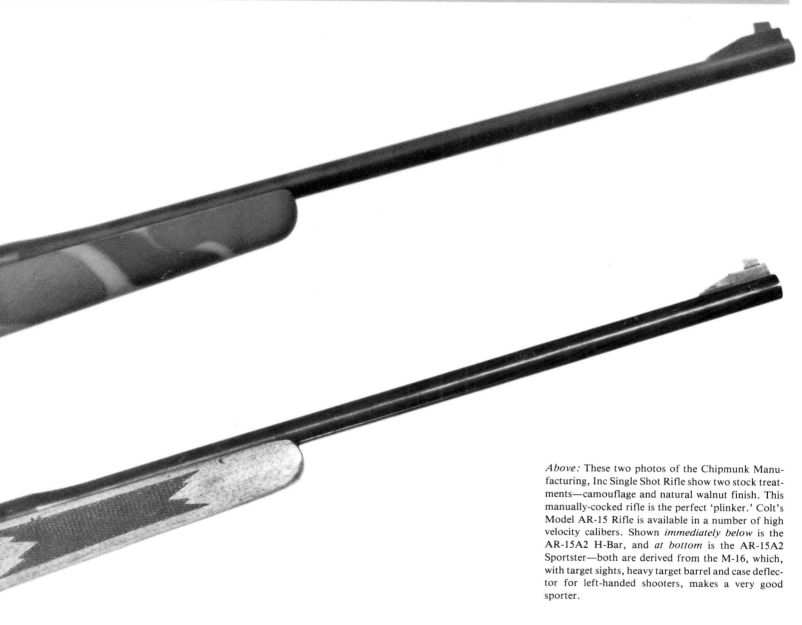

Above: These two photos of the Chipmunk Manufacturing, Inc Single Shot Rifle show two stock treatments—camouflage and natural walnut finish. This manually-cocked rifle is the perfect 'plinker.' Colt's Model AR-15 Rifle is available in a number of high velocity calibers. Shown *immediately below* is the AR-15A2 H-Bar, and *at bottom* is the AR-15A2 Sportster—both are derived from the M-16, which, with target sights, heavy target barrel and case deflector for left-handed shooters, makes a very good sporter.

This page, in descending order: Hopkins & Allen's percussion cap and flintlock rifles: the Buggy Rifle is a light, fast 'brush country' underhammer; the Deerstalker is a heavy bore underhammer; the Plainsman has windage-adjustable sights and a solid brass rib barrel; the Schuetzen is a hand crafted match grade target rifle; the Target Rifle is designed for use at a bench rest; and the Tryon Trailblazer is a reproduction of the George Tryon Plainsrifle of the 1820s. *Right:* The sleek Marlin 444 SS.

The Hopkins & Allen **Brush Rifle** is available as a flintlock or percussion muzzleloader. Designed for stalking game, it is offered in kit or finished model form.

Buggy Rifle

Type: Muzzleloading underhammer
Caliber: .31–.36 and .45
Barrel Length: 20″ or 25″
Weight: 6–7 lbs
Stock: Hardwood with blued barrel and
　　　　receiver
Ideal for chasing game in heavily wooded country, the **Buggy Rifle** is a light, fast pointing gun similar to the short-barrel carbines of the 1840s that were made to carry in wagons and buggies.

Deerstalker Rifle

Type: Muzzleloading underhammer
Caliber: .58
Barrel Length: 28″
Weight: 9.5 lbs
Stock: Hardwood with blued barrel and
　　　　receiver
Rifled at one turn in 72″, the **Deerstalker's** .575 bore will handle a 580 grain slug for optimum hunting knockdown power.

Heritage Rifle

Type: Muzzleloading underhammer
Caliber: .31, .36, .45, .50
Barrel Length: 32″
Weight: 7.5 to 8 lbs
Stock: Hardwood with blued barrel and
　　　　receiver

Pennsylvania Hawken Rifle

Type: Muzzleloader
Caliber: .50
Barrel Length: 29″
Weight: 7.5 lbs
Length: 44″ overall
Stock: Walnut with cheek piece
Available in both percussion and flintlock models, the **Pennsylvania Hawken Rifle** is equipped with a classic single trigger and dual barrel wedges for added strength. Special features include its convertible ignition, brass patch box and heavy duty ramrod. This Hopkins & Allen muzzleloader is also available in kit form.

Plainsman Rifle

Type: Muzzleloading long gun
Caliber: .45
Barrel Length: 37″

Weight: 7.5 lbs
Length: 53″ overall
Stock: Walnut
Features of this half stock rifle are its double set triggers, sight adjustable for windage and elevation, and the solid brass rib barrel and engraved lock. Available in percussion only.

Schuetzen Rifle

Type: Muzzleloading long gun
Caliber: .45
Barrel Length: 29″
Weight: 10 lbs
Length: 44″ overall
Stock: Walnut with cheek piece
For the discriminating target shooter, a hand crafted match rifle that accepts round ball or bullet ammunition. The rear sight is aperture type, tang mounted and adjusted for windage and elevation.

Target Rifle

Type: Muzzleloading underhammer
Caliber: .45
Barrel Length: 42″
Weight: 14 lbs
Stock: Hardwood with blued barrel and
　　　　receiver

An underhammer rifle designed for target shooting, the Hopkins & Allen **Target** model omits barrel forend or ramrod ferrules and makes an ideal bench rest gun.

Tryon Trailblazer Rifle

Type: Muzzleloading long gun
Caliber: .54
Barrel Length: 32″
Weight: 9 lbs
Length: 48″ overall
Stock: European walnut with cheek piece
A reproduction of a George Tryon Plains rifle designed in the 1820s, the Hopkins & Allen

Trailblazer features double set triggers, back action lock, and hook breech with long tang.

Ljutic Industries, Inc

Ljutic Recoiless Space Rifle

Type: Single shot
Caliber: .308, .30-06, .30-30, and .22-250
Weight: 8.75 lbs, 9.25 lbs with scope
The single shot Ljutic **Space Rifle** with its patented in-line design reduces normal recoil by 50% and its stock configuration makes the gun come up better and shoot with in-

creased accuracy. The pushbutton trigger can be adjusted for desired speeds and weights. The entire gun is made up of 6 heavy duty parts including the standard stock, 14.75″ in length.

The Marlin Firearms Co

Marlin Big Game Rifles

Caliber: .45/70 (Model 1895SS); 444 Marlin (Model 444SS); 356 Win (Model 336ER)
Barrel Length: 22″ (Models 1895SS and 444SS); 20″ (Model 336ER)

Weight: 7.5 lbs (Models 1895SS and 444SS); 6.75 lbs (Model 336ER)

Length: 40.5" overall (Models 1895SS and 444SS); 38.5" overall (Model 336ER)

Stock: American black walnut

Magazine Capacity: 4 rounds (Model 1895SS); 5 rounds (Models 444SS and 336ER)

Marlin's **Model 1895SS**'s strong, modified 336 action easily handles the powerful load of its big game heavy-cover cartridge. The **Model 444SS** Marlin combines the knock-down power of the big 444 cartridge with a quick, smooth Marlin lever action system. Lastly, the **Model 336ER** (Extra Range) Marlin has been designed to give optimum performance on game ranges well beyond 200 yards. All 3 Big Game models feature a lever action, solid top receiver, side ejection, hammer block safety, adjustable folding rear sight, and ramp front sight with brass bead.

Marlin Bolt Action 22 Magnum

Caliber: .22 Win Magnum Rim Fire

Barrel Length: 22"

Weight: 6 lbs

Length: 41" overall

Stock: American black walnut (Models 782, 783); hardwood (Model 25M)

Magazine Capacity: 7-shot clip (Models 782, 25M); 12-shot tubular (Model 783)

Offered as a 7-shot clip **Model 782** and a 12-shot tubular **Model 783**, the upscale Marlin bolt action .22 Magnums feature a Monte Carlo black walnut stock, full pistol grip and classic checkering, leather carrying strap, and bolt action with a serrated, anti-glare receiver top. The more economical **Model 25M** with 7-shot clip sports a walnut finished hardwood stock, and bolt action with thumb safety and a red cocking indicator.

Marlin Bolt Action 22 Rifle

Caliber: .22 Short, Long, or Long Rifle

Barrel Length: 22" (Models 780, 781, 25); 16.25" (Model 15Y)

Weight: 4.25–6 lbs

Length: 41" overall (Models 780, 781, 25); 33.25" overall (Model 15Y)

Stock: Black walnut (Models 780, 781); walnut hardwood (Models 25, 15Y)

Magazine Capacity: 7-shot clip (Models 780, 25); single shot (Model 15Y); tubular magazine holding 25 shorts, 19 longs, or 17 long rifles (Model 781)

Ranging from **Models 780** and **25** with 7-shot clips and **Model 781** with its large capacity tubular magazine to the single shot 'Little Buckaroo' **Model 15Y**, there's a full range of bolt action Marlin .22s. The youth-size 15Y has an easy-load feed throat, thumb

safety, and red cocking indicator. Sights on the 15Y and 25 models are adjustable open rear and ramp front. Models 780 and 781 have adjustable folding rear and ramp front sight with brass bead.

Marlin Center Fire Semi-Automatic Carbines

Caliber: .45 ACP (Model 45); 9mm Luger (Model 9)
Barrel Length: 16.5"
Weight: 6.75 lbs
Length: 35.5" overall
Stock: Walnut finished hardwood
Magazine Capacity: 7-shot clip (Model 45); 12-shot clip and 20-shot magazine available (Model 9)

Designed as a sporting carbine, Marlin's center fire semi-automatics start with the **Model 45**. This rifle fills the need for a classic-lined sporting carbine chambered for the ever-popular .45 automatic cartridge. Its receiver is machined from a block of steel, then drilled and tapped for a scope.

Like its .45 counterpart, the **Model 9** is a small game gun that is tailored for 9mm caliber ammunition. Both models feature a magazine disconnect, 'last shot' automatic bolt hold-open and a manual bolt hold-open for safety. Sights are adjustable folding rear and ramp front with brass bead.

Marlin Lever Action 22 Rifle

Caliber: .22 Short, Long, or Long Rifle

Barrel Length: 24" (Golden 39A), 20" (Golden 39M)
Weight: 6.5 lbs (Golden 39A); 6 lbs (Golden 39M)
Length: 40" overall (Golden 39A); 36" overall (Golden 39M)
Stock: American black walnut
Magazine Capacity: Golden 39A—26 short, 21 long, 19 long rifle Golden 39M—21 short, 16 long, 15 long rifle

Marlin's full pistol grip **Golden 39A** has a solid top receiver, side ejection, one-step take down, gold plated steel trigger, adjustable rear sight, and ramp front sight. The shorter barreled and lighter-weight **Golden 39M** combines the same features as the Golden 39A with a squared finger lever and a straight grip.

Marlin Model 30AS Rifle

Caliber: .30/30 Win
Barrel Length: 20"
Weight: 7 lbs
Length: 38.25" overall
Stock: Walnut finished hardwood
Magazine Capacity: 6 rounds

Marlin describes their **Model 30AS Deer Rifle** as a 'gutsy, no frills' .30/30 with traditional styling. This lever action, side ejection rifle has an adjustable rear sight and a brass bead front sight, solid top receiver, and off-set hammer spur for right or left handed scope use.

These 3 Marlins *(at top, in descending order)* are based on the famous Marlin side ejection, solid receiver lever action design: the .45-70 Government 1895 SS; the .444 Marlin 444 SS; and the .356 Winchester 336 ER. Marlin Semi-Automatic Carbines include the New Model 45 *(above)* in .45 ACP; and the Model 9 *(left)* in 9mm Luger. *Top right:* A Marlin lever action in .375 Winchester. *Right, from top to bottom:* the Marlin Model 990 .22 semi-automatic, the Marlin Golden 39A .22 lever action; and the 444 SS.

Marlin Model 336 Deer Rifle

Caliber: .30/30 Win (Models CS and TS); .35 Rem or .375 Win (Model CS)

Barrel Length: 20″ (Model CS); 18.5″ (Model TS)

Weight: 7 lbs (Model CS); 6.5 lbs (Model TS)

Length: 38.5″ overall (Model CS); 37″ overall (Model TS)

Stock: American black walnut

Magazine Capacity: 6 rounds

Marlin lever action **Model 336 Deer Rifles** are available in the pistol grip carbine style **336CS** and the western straight grip carbine style **336TS**. Both versions feature a hammer block safety, solid steel forgings, a solid-top side ejecting receiver. Sights consist of an adjustable semi-buckhorn folding rear and a ramp front sight with brass bead and 'wide-scan' hood.

Marlin Model 1894 Magnum Rifle

Caliber: .22 Win Mag Rim Fire (Model 1894M); .44 Rem Mag/.44S&W Special (Model 1894S) .357 Mag and .38 Special (Model 1894CS)

Barrel Length: 20″ (Models M and S); 18.5″ (Model CS)

Weight: 6.25 lbs (Model M); 6 lbs (Models S and CS)

Length: 37.5″ overall (Models M and S); 36″ overall (Model CS)

Stock: American black walnut

Magazine Capacity: 11 rounds (Model M); 10 rounds (Model S); 9 rounds (Model CS)

The Marlin **Model 1894M** has been built around an action that goes back nearly 90 years. Perfect for small game and informal target shooting, it has a solid top receiver, side ejection, and hammer block safety. The **1894S**'s terrific knockdown power makes this rifle a good companion to handguns of the same caliber. With a straight grip stock and square bolt, it has the same look and heft as the original 1894. Marlin's **Model 1894CS** puts a shorter barrel onto this balanced, fast-handling carbine. It has 6 solid steel forgings and a 9-shot tubular magazine.

Marlin Semi-Automatic .22 with Clip Magazine

Caliber: .22 LR

Barrel Length: 16.25″ (Model 70P); 18″ (Models 70 and 995)

Weight: 3.75 lbs (Model 70P); 5 lbs (Models 70 and 995)

Length: 35.25″–36.75″ overall

Stock: Walnut finished hardwood (Models 70P and 70); Black walnut (995)

Magazine Capacity: 7-shot clip

Models 70P and **70** are similar except in their barrel lengths, minor stock differences, and the fact that the 70P is a take-down gun.

(The 70P 'Papoose' comes with a padded carrying case and 4x scope.) Both models have adjustable open rear and ramp front sights and a receiver grooved for tip-off scope mount. The **Model 995** is distinguished by its American black walnut stock and adjustable folding rear and ramp front with brass bead sights. All 3 models have a side ejection action, manual bolt hold-open, and cross-bolt safety.

Marlin Semi-Automatic 22 with Tubular Magazine

Caliber: .22 LR
Barrel Length: 22″ (Models 990 and 60); 18″ (Model 75C)
Weight: 5.5 lbs (Models 990 and 60); 5 lbs (Model 75C)
Length: 40.5″ overall (Models 990 and 60); 36.5″ overall (Model 75C)
Stock: American black walnut (Model 990); hardwood (Models 60 and 75C)
Magazine Capacity: 17 rounds (Models 990 and 60); 13 rounds (Model 75C)

Marlin semi-automatic tubular magazine .22s have simple, fast actions that are known for their reliability. The **Model 990** and the **Model 60** feature a .22″ 'Micro-Groove' rifled barrel, folding rear sight, ramp front sight, cross-bolt safety, and both manual and automatic bolt hold-opens. **Model 75C** with its walnut finished hardwood stock, 18″ barrel, and 13-shot magazine has an adjustable open rear sight, ramp front sight, and a receiver grooved for tip-off scope mount.

Mitchell Arms

Centerfire AK-47 Rifle

Type: Semi-automatic
Caliber: 7.62mm
Stock: Solid teak
Magazine Capacity: 30 rounds

With a semi-automatic receiver and action, the heavy barrel **AK-47** features a finned barrel, adjustable day or night sights and a scope mount rail for detachable scope mount. A second, folding stock, model has a steel folding buttstock that can be used with the stock foled or extended. Steel drum magazines of 75 rounds are available for both AK-47s.

Counter-Sniper M-76 Rifle

Type: Semi-automatic
Caliber: 7.9mm
Magazine Capacity: 10 rounds

The Mitchell Arms' **M-76** is advertised as an anti-terrorist rifle for police. Based on the AK-47 action, the M-76 has a non-slip ribber butt plate, a detachable steel box magazine with a last round hold-open, and a passive night sight.

Mitchell Arms Combat Rifle

Type: Semi-automatic
Caliber: .22 LR or .22 Mag
Stock: Walnut

Mitchell Arms **Combat Rifle** is inspired by the Galil combat weapon. It has fully adjustable sights, a walnut pistol grip, walnut stock and forend, flash hider, and a wide magazine to maintain appearance. A scope mount is available separately.

Mitchell Arms M-59 Rifle

Type: Gas-operated semi-automatic
Caliber: 7.62mm
Stock: Walnut
Sights: Fully adjustable

Rimfire AK-22 Rifle

Type: Semi-automatic
Caliber: .22 LR and .22 Mag
Stock: European walnut
Sights: Fully adjustable

Faithful to the design of the Mitchell Arms AK-47, the **AK-22** is accurate and inexpensive to shoot. It features a full wide magazine to maintain appearance, pistol grip, deluxe forend, and built-in cleaning rod.

Marlin models—*above, top to bottom:* The Model 782, 7 shot .22 Magnum; the Model 783, 12 shot .22 Magnum; the Model 25M, 7 shot .22 Rimfire; the Model 70P semi-automatic; the Model 70 semi-automatic; and the Model 995 semi-automatic. *At right:* The Marlin 70P 'Papoose' breaks down easily for portability.

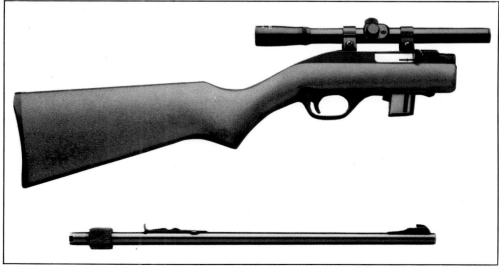

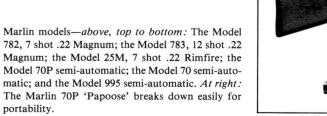

OF Mossberg

Mossberg Centerfire Rifle

Type: Bolt action repeating
Caliber: .223 to .338 Win Mag
Barrel Length: 22"
Weight: 7 lbs to 7.10 lbs
Length: 42" overall
Stock: Select walnut
Magazine Capacity: 5 or 6 rounds

Mossberg **Model 1500/1700 Centerfire Rifles** are part of the Mossberg 'Select Series.' Accuracy, performance, and variety of caliber, sights, and finishes are the important features of this series of bolt action rifles. All models have a positive, non-slip thumb type safety, machined steel bolt with twin locking lugs riding on a three rail design, cold hammer forged steel barrel, and select walnut stock. The new Model 1550 features a removable magazine for safe, convenient loading and unloading. A special **Model 1600 Deluxe Varmint** version weighs in at a strapping 9.5 lbs.

Mossberg Law Enforcement/Security Model 1500 Rifle

Type: Repeating bolt action
Caliber: .223 Rem or .308 Win

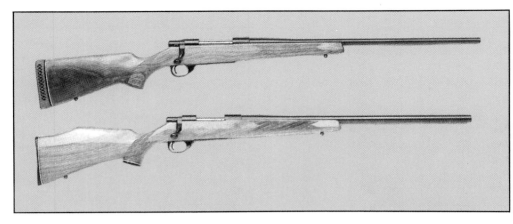

Barrel Length: 24"
Weight: 9.5 lbs
Length: 44" overall
Stock: Select walnut
Magazine Capacity: 6 rounds (.223) and 5 rounds (.308)

Designed to sharpshooting specifications, the **Model 1500** is equipped with optics that can provide pin-point shot placement. The action bolt is of machined steel with twin locking lugs and three gas relief ports; the trigger is adjustable for travel and weight. This specialized rifle has a 13.5" length of pull, .75" drop at comb, .56" drop at Monte Carlo, and 1.38" drop at heel.

Mowrey Gun Works, Inc

Mowrey 1N30 Muzzleloading Rifle

Type: Box-lock muzzleloader
Caliber: .45, .50, and .54
Weight: 8 lbs (.45); 10 lbs (.50 and .54)

The Mowrey **1N30** is designed for conical style bullets such as the Buffalo bullet. Based on a 19th century design, it has a two moving part action (the trigger and tumbler). The stock and forearm are curly maple.

Mowrey Little Tex Muzzleloading Rifle

Type: Box-lock muzzleloader
Caliber: .36 and .45

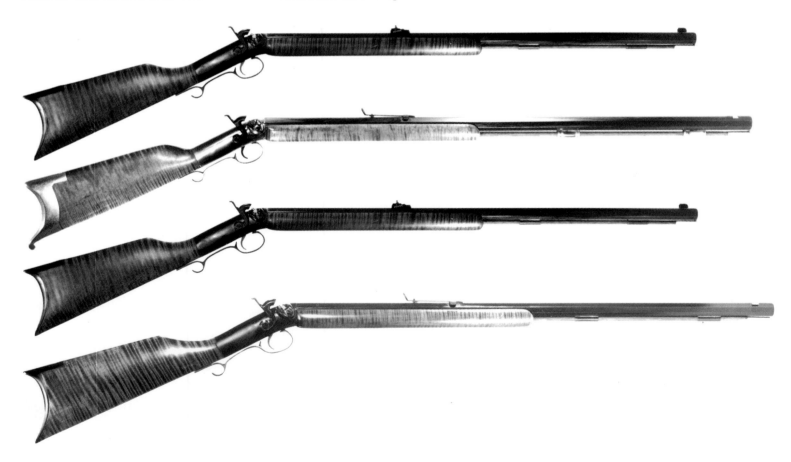

Top of page: These 2 rifles are Mossberg Model 1500 bolt actions, which feature accuracy, performance and outstanding finish. Mowrey Muzzleloaders feature curly maple stocks—as their ancestors often did. *Above, top to bottom:* The Mowrey IN30 conical bullet rifle; the Plains Rifle, a repro of an Ethan Allen design; the Rocky Mountain Hunter with adjustable sights; and the hand-fitted, boxlock Squirrel Rifle. *Opposite, top:* The Navy Arms Hawken Rifle is made for left-handers; and *below it,* the Navy Arms Morse Muzzleloader features precision rifling and a 'pre-straightened' barrel for accuracy. *At right:* The .22 caliber Remington Model 541T Sporter. Remington bolt action .22s have punctured many a tin can.

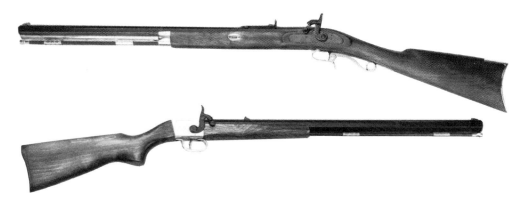

Barrel Length: 20″
Weight: Approx. 5.5 lbs
Stock: Premium grade curly maple
Mowrey's **Little Tex** has a 10″ trigger pull and is scaled for the younger or smaller frame shooter.

Mowrey Plains Muzzleloading Rifle

Type: Box-lock muzzleloader
Caliber: .50 or .54
Barrel Length: 32″
Weight: 10 lbs (.50 cal.) and 11 lbs (.54 cal.)
Stock: Premium grade curly maple
A recreation of an Ethan Allen designed gun marketed under the name Allen & Thurber in 1835, the **Plains Rifle** features a two moving part box-lock action, a fully adjustable trigger, front German silver blade sight and adjustable semi-buckhorn rear sight.

Mowrey Rocky Mountain Hunter Muzzleloader

Type: Box-lock muzzleloader
Caliber: .50 or .54
Barrel Length: 28″
Stock: Premium grade curly maple
The Mowrey **Rocky Mountain Hunter** is designed for early season or special season hunters. Made of an all browned steel frame and furniture, it has rear notch white dot blade sights that are adjustable for windage and elevation.

Mowrey Squaw Gun

Type: Box-lock muzzleloader
Caliber: .36 and .45
Barrel Length: 25″
Weight: 6 lbs
Stock: Premium grade curly maple
Recently added to the Mowrey black powder line, the **Squaw Gun** is designed for a woman's frame—with a 12.5″ pull.

Mowrey Squirrel Muzzleloading Rifle

Type: Box-lock muzzleloader
Caliber: .36 or .45
Barrel Length: 28″
Weight: 7 lbs
The Mowrey **Squirrel Rifle** is based on the rugged 19th century Allen and Thurber box-lock design. Its action has only two moving parts, the barrels are made from quality steel, and the rifle is available with brass or browned steel frame. Each gun is separately hand-fitted to the barrel stock and forearm using all American made materials.

Navy Arms Company

Ithaca/Navy Left Hand Hawken Rifle

Type: Muzzleloader
Caliber: .50
Barrel Length: 31.5″
Stock: Pennsylvania black walnut

Navy Arms' left handed **Hawken** muzzleloading rifle is made in the USA with a 'pre-straightened' .50 cal barrel, percussion left lock with V-mainspring and solid brass furniture.

Morse Muzzleloading Rifle

Type: Muzzleloader
Caliber: .50
Barrel Length: 26″
Weight: 6 lbs
Length: 41.5″ overall
Navy Arms calls this percussion muzzleloader an ideal primitive-weapon hunting rifle. It features a precision rifled 'Pre-straightened' Navy Arms barrel assuring the shooter the best possible accuracy. The action is highly polished brass and the barrel is precision rifled with a barrel twist of 1 in 48″.

Remington Arms Company, Inc

Remington Autoloading Rifles

Type: Autoloading
Caliber: .243 and .270 Win, .280 Rem, .30-06 Spfd, and .308 Win (7400 only)
Barrel Length: 22″
Weight: 7.5 lbs
Length: 42″

Stock: American walnut
Magazine Capacity: 4-shot clip
Remington's two autoloading repeating rifles feature the same mechanical design and are distinguished by the more expensive custom features built into the high power Model Four. The **Model Four** has a Monte Carlo style stock with full cheekpiece, curved pistol grip, flared forend and positive cut checkering. It also sports a cartridge head imbedded in steel just forward of the receiver. Its sights are detachable: ramp front with flat-faced gold heads, rear adjustable for windage and elevation.
The **Model 7400** autoloader has the same proven action with white-line spacers, a walnut stock with high-gloss finish, and custom checkering. Model 7400 sights are also detachable.

Remington Model 700 Big Game Rifles

Type: Centerfire bolt action
Caliber: .17 Rem to .280 Rem; 6mm to 7mm Rem/Rem Mag, .264 Rem Mag to .300 Win Mag
Barrel Length: 22″ and 24″
Weight: 6.75 lbs ('Mountain Rifle') to 9 lbs. ('Varmint Special')
Length: 42.5″ to 44.5″
Stock: American walnut
Magazine Capacity: 3 to 5 rounds

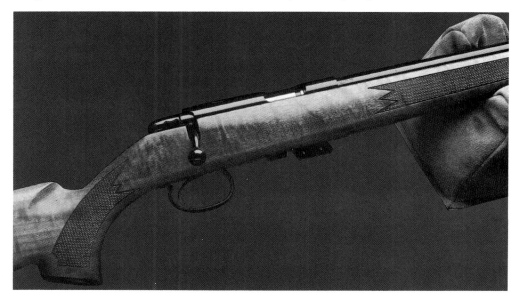

With its bolt action strength and accuracy, the **Model 700** series offers a wide range of rifles, all with an extremely fast lock time and crisp trigger. The **Mountain Rifle** is a recent addition to the line, sporting a 22″ barrel and trim, lighter weight overall size. Both the **Model 700BDL** and heavy-barreled **Varmint Special** feature a Monte Carlo style American walnut stock with cheekpiece, positive cut skip line checkering, hinged floorplate and quick release swivel studs.

A yearly **Classic** model, chambered in a classic caliber for a limited production run, features a traditional straight line stock, full-pattern cut checkering, satin wood finish, brown rubber butt pad, sling swivel studs and hinged floorplate. The value-leading **Model 700ADL** also has cut checkering on an American walnut stock and a hand-applied satin finish. All Model 700s are factory drilled and tapped for scope mounts. Except for a few of the Varmint calibers, blade ramp front sights and fully adjustable rear sights come with all Model 700ADLs and BDLs. BDL front sights are hooded and removable.

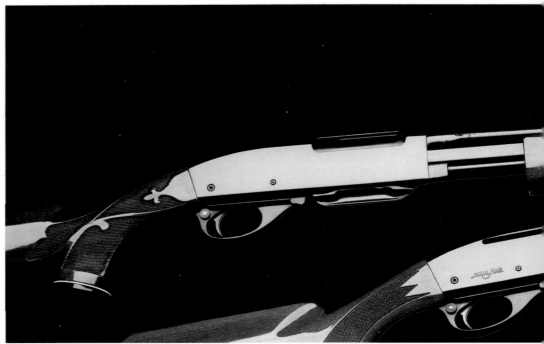

The Remington **Model 7** is a lightweight (6.25 lbs) and compact (37.5″ overall) bolt action centerfire rifle that completes the 700 series. Offered in five short action calibers including the 7mm-08 Rem and .223 Rem, the Model 7 also features an 18.5″ tapered barrel with ramp front, adjustable rear sights and hinged floorplate.

Remington Pump Action Rifles

Type: Pump action
Caliber: .243 and .270 Win .30-06 Spfd and .30-06 Accelerator, .308 Win and .308 Accelerator
Barrel Length: 22″
Weight: 7.5 lbs
Length: 42″ overall
Stock: American walnut
Magazine Capacity: 4-shot clip

Remington's two pump-action repeating rifles are the high power **Model Six** and the

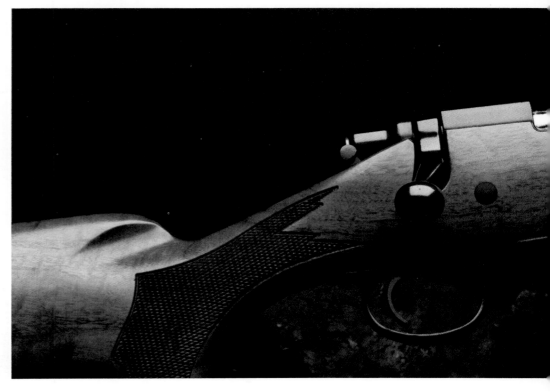

The legendary Remington 700 series Mountain Rifle *(top and bottom left)* is available in a wide variety of big game calibers, and has newly had its weight pared by way of a slenderer stock and tapered barrel. The Remington Model 7600 Pump Action Rifle *(lower left)* features the famous Remington pump mechanism, and the Remington Model 4 Autoloader *(middle left)* is another outstanding Remington sports rifle.

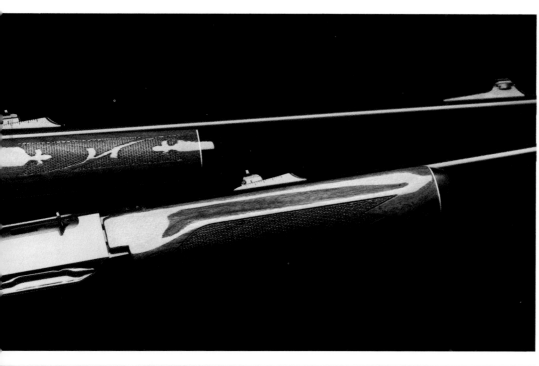

Model 7600. Both known for their highly responsive double action bars, the major difference between the two models are the quality touches that have been added to the Model Six. It features positive-cut checkering on the Monte Carlo style stock, full cheekpiece, curved pistol grip and flared forearm for control. The Model Six also has detachable sights with flat-faced front beads and a bolt with massive locking lugs similar to those of bolt action rifles.

The Model 7600 has the same proven action as the Model Six but is less expensive in design. Its primary features are white-line spacers, walnut stock with a high-gloss finish, custom checkering, and detachable sights.

Remington Rimfire Autoloader 'Nylon 66'
Type: Repeating autoloader
Caliber: .22
Barrel Length: 19-5/8"
Weight: 4 lbs
Length: 38.5" overall
Stock: 'Zytel' nylon
Magazine Capacity: 15 rounds

The **Nylon 66** model is based on a new design concept in which the forend, receiver, and buttstock are made in one piece of Du-Pont 'Zytel' nylon. Friction-free steel parts ride on nylon bearings and need no lubrication. The stock itself is fully warranted not to warp, crack, chip, fade or peel.

Remington Rimfire Bolt Action 541T Sporter
Type: Bolt action
Caliber: .22
Barrel Length: 24"
Weight: 5.88 lbs
Length: 42.5" overall
Stock: American wanut
Magazine Capacity: 5 shot clip

The **Model 571T** Sporter for bolt action shooters features an American walnut stock with cut checkering and a quality satin finish. The receiver is drilled and tapped for

Above: The .22 caliber, 5-shot Remington Sportsman 581 is an almost archetypal 'plinking' rifle, and has killed many a tin can. *Below, top to bottom:* The Remington Sportsman 74 autoloader's gas metering system reduces recoil; the Sportsman 76 pump action is fast and smooth; the Sportsman 581S is chambered for .22 caliber. *Opposite:* Remington Models 700 (bolt action) and 6 (pump).

scope mounting and its 5 shot clip magazine handles short, long, and long rifle cartridges.

Remington Rimfire Fieldmaster Models 572/572BDL

Type: Repeating pump action
Caliber: .22

Barrel Length: 21″
Weight: 5.5 lbs
Length: 40″ overall
Magazine Capacity: 15 LR cartridges
The pump action **572 Fieldmaster** with 21″ barrel is styled for better balance with a narrower pistol grip stock section and big game rifle sights with bead front and fully adjustable rear. The 572 shoots short, long, and long rifle cartridges interchangeably and can be converted to single shot by removing the inner magazine tube. The **Deluxe Grade 572BDL** features a custom checkered walnut stock, blade ramp front sight and sliding ramp rear sight for more precise range adjustment. Other specs are those of the model 572.

Remington Rimfire Speedmaster Models 552/552BDL

Type: Repeating autoloader
Caliber: .22
Barrel Length: 21″
Weight: 5.5 lbs
Length: 40″ overall
Magazine Capacity: 15 LR cartridges
Remington's **Standard Grade Autoloader Model 552** features a narrower pistol grip stock section and big game rifle sights. Interchangeable short, long, and long rifle cartridge capability is featured along with this

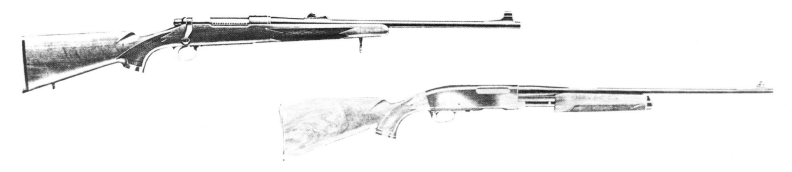

rifle's crossbolt safety switch, half pistol grip stock and semi-beavertail forend. The **Deluxe Grade 552BDL** combines the same features with a stylish checkered walnut stock, blade-ramp front sight and sliding-ramp rear sight for more precise range adjustment.

Remington Sportsman 74 Autoloader Rifle

Type: Autoloading centerfire
Caliber: .30-06 Spfd
Barrel Length: 22"
Weight: 7.5 lbs
Length: 42" overall
Stock: Walnut-finished hardwood
Magazine Capacity: 4 rounds
The **Sportsman 74** model offers quick, extra shot performance, balance, and expert accuracy. Its bolt has massive locking lugs similar to those of bolt action rifles and its receiver is drilled and tapped for scope mounts. The gas metering system reduces recoil sensations.

Remington Sportsman 76 Pump-Action Rifle

Type: Pump action centerfire
Caliber: .30-06 Spfd
Barrel Length: 22"
Weight: 7.5 lbs
Length: 42" overall
Stock: Walnut finished hardwood
Magazine Capacity: 4 rounds
This **Sportsman** pump action model provides a fast second shot performance without your eyes leaving the target. It possesses fast and smooth double action bars that slide with little effort. Sights consist of a detachable ramp front and step rear.

Remington Sportsman Bolt Action Rifles

Type: Bolt action centerfire (model 78); bolt action rimfire (model 581)
Caliber: .223 Rem .243-308 Win .30-06 Sprg (78); .22 (581)
Barrel Length: 22" to 24"
Weight: 9.25 lbs to 12 lbs
Length: 41.5" to 43.5"
Stock: American hardwood

Magazine Capacity: 4 rounds (model 78); 5 rounds (model 581)
Chambered for 4 calibers, the **Sportsman 78** model features a straight comb walnut-finished hardwood stock and rounded forend. The sights are adjustable and the receiver is drilled and tapped for easy scope mounting. The **Model 581** rimfire bolt action combines Remington's strong, proven action with the highly accurate .22 caliber.

Remington Target 40-XB/40-XBBR Centerfire Rifles

Type: Bolt action, single shot and repeating
Caliber: .222 Rem to .300 Win Mag
Barrel Length: 27.25"
Weight: 9.75 lbs average
Length: 45.75" overall
Stock: American walnut
Magazine Capacity: Single loading and clip repeater
The Remington **Rangemaster 40-XB** and accompanying **Benchrest Model 40-XBBR** offer benchrest and position shooters a stainless steel barrel in calibers from .222 Rem to .300 Win Mag. Available in single shot or repeater, the 40-XB features a free floating barrel, high comb that is grooved for easy bolt removal and a hand-bedded action. Both the 40-XB and 40-XBBR single shot have a wide match-type externally adjustable trigger that changes weight of pull and eliminates creep and overtravel.

Remington Target 40-XC/40-XR Bolt-Action Rifles

Type: Bolt-action centerfire and rimfire
Caliber: 7.62mm Nato (40-XC) and .22 LR (40-XR)
Barrel Length: 24"
Weight: 11 lbs (40-XC); 9.25 lbs (40-XR)
Length: 43.5" overall (40-XC); 42.5" overall (40-XR)
Magazine Capacity: 5 rounds
Remington **Match Course 40-XC Repeater** and **Rimfire Single Shot 40-XR** models have improved position stocks for an extra competitive edge. Their pistol-grip shape eliminates wrist-twisting and assures straight-back trigger finger pull, permitting easier

mounting of the stock to the shoulder. With a 13.5" length of pull, the 40-XC meets International Shooting Union rules for army rifles with fixed sling swivel added; the 40-XR meets those same rules for standard rifle specifications.

Savage Industries, Inc

Savage Series 24 Combination Rifles/Shotguns

Type: Break action centerfire and rimfire rifles with 2nd barrel shotgun
Barrel Length: 24" centerfire, 20" rimfire
Weight: 5.75 lbs to 7 lbs
Length: 36.5" to 40.5"
Stock: Walnut finish hardwood
The centerfire rifle/shotgun **Model 24-V** is Savage's best known combination gun. It features a pistol grip and slim line forend and sports a fixed front sight with rear sight adjustable for elevation. The top barrel is available in .222, .223 Rem., and .30-30 calibers. The bottom barrel is 20 ga. Savage's lightweight **Model 24 Field** is a rimfire rifle/shotgun combination that is chambered for .22 LR over .410 bore or 20 ga. and .22 WMR over 20 ga. **Model 24-C** with break action and bottom opening lever is available in a .22 LR over 20 ga combination. It has an ammunition storage compartment built into the Monte Carlo style stock.

Savage Series 110 Bolt Action Rifles

Type: Centerfire, bolt action
Caliber: .233 Rem, .243, .270 Win, .30-06, 7mm Rem Mag, .338 Win Mag
Barrel Length: 22" to 24" (26" Varmint Model)
Weight: 6.75 lbs to 7 lbs (Mag); 9 lbs Varmint Model
Length: 43.5" to 45.5" overall (46.5" Varmint Model)
Stock: Walnut
Magazine Capacity: 4 rounds with 1 in chamber
Strong bolt action hunting rifles that feature top loading internal box magazine for sure-fire loading, the **Model 110-D** standard features a detachable hood ramp front sight and

At top: The Savage Model 99C lever action is available in .243 or .308 Winchester calibers and its clip magazine is designed to permit easy chambering of these cartridges. The extremely simple Savage Industries' Stevens Model 72 Crackshot *(mid-page)* falling-block rifle in .22 caliber is ideal for beginners. The Savage Model 110-V Varmint Rifle *(immediately above)* has an internal box magazine, a heavy target barrel and is tapped for scope mounting. *Right, above:* The Savage Model 24-C over-and-under 'Camper's Companion' is designed with a .22 Long Rifle barrel over a 20 gauge shotgun barrel. *Right, below:* The Model 24-V is available with a .223 Remington, .243 or .270 Winchester barrel over a 20 gauge shotgun barrel.

Sharps Arms' fine heavy caliber black powder models include *(above, from the top)* the Number 3 Standard Sporter with tang sight; the Deluxe Sporter, a cartridge rifle featuring a traditional cheek rest buttstock; and the very handy Saddle Rifle.

an ajustable rear sight. The **Model 110-DL** is the left-handed version with bolt opening and ejecting from the left hand side.

Available in 7 different calibers including 7mm Mag, the **Model 110-E** bolt action has the same internal box magazine and swivel studs as the 110-D but combines those features with a front bead sight and rear sight removable and adjustable for windage and elevation. The **110-V Varmint Model** with its greater size has a 26″ barrel, varmint style stock, and is tapped for scope mounting. It's available in calibers.22-.250 and.223 Rem.

Savage Model 99-C Lever Action Rifle

Type: Centerfire, lever action
Caliber: .243 and .308 Win
Barrel Length: 22″
Weight: 7 lbs
Length: 42.75″ overall
Stock: Select walnut
Magazine Capacity: 4 round detachable clip with one in chamber

The clip magazine on this centerfire rifle allows for the chambering of pointed, high velocity big bore cartridges. The action is hammerless with a cocking indicator and top tang safety. Other features on the Savage **99-C** are the cut checkered walnut stock with recoil pad, detachable hooded ramp front sight and adjustable rear sight.

Stevens Rimfire Model 72 Crackshot Rifle

Type: Single shot, falling block lever action
Caliber: .22 LR
Barrel Length: 22″
Weight: 4.5 lbs
Length: 37″ overall
Stock: Walnut

This lightweight, single shot rifle from Savage Industries finds its popularity with novice hunters and shooters. It has a black metal frame and sports a fixed front sight with rear sight adjustable for elevation.

Stevens Rimfire Model 987 Autoloading Rifle

Type: Autoloader
Caliber: .22 LR
Barrel Length: 20″
Weight: 6 lbs
Length: 40.5″ overall
Stock: Walnut finished hardwood
Magazine Capacity: 15 rounds

The Stevens **Model 987** by Savage has a pistol grip and hard rubber butt plate. It has a bead front sight with dovetail mount and a rear sight adjustable for elevation.

Serrifile, Inc

Due to an inability to renew their liability insurance, Serrifile, Inc is no longer produc-

ing complete rifles and pistols. Production of replacement parts for their **Schuetzen Rifle** and **Terrier One** pistol is, however, ongoing.

C Sharps Arms Co, Inc

Model 1863 Breech Loading Percussion Rifles

Caliber: .54
Barrel Length: 22″ and 30″
Weight: 9 lbs (30″)

Sharps' **Model 1863** has a tapered octagonal barrel, blade front sight, sporting rear sight with elevation leaf and double set triggers with an adjustable set. The buttstock has a traditional straight grip; powder capacity is 100 grains. Besides the **Standard Sporting Rifle**, this gun is also offered as a **Military Rifle** with a 30″ barrel and a **Military Carbine** with a 22″ barrel.

Model 1874 Breech Loading Black Powder Metallic Cartridge Rifles

Caliber: .40-50 to .50-140
Barrel Length: 24″ to 34″
Weight: 9 lbs to 12.5 lbs
Length: to 51″ overall
Stock: Black walnut

In octagonal barreled models ranging from the **Saddle Rifle** (26″) to the **Long Range**

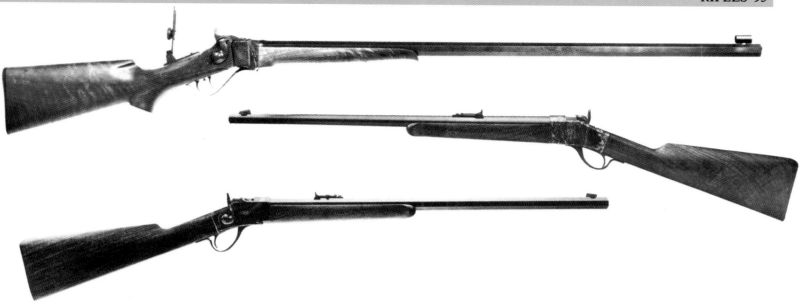

Express (34″), these black powder, metallic cartridge rifles have double-set adjustable triggers and oil finished black walnut stocks. The **Standard Sporter** with 30″ barrel has a straight grip buttstock with rifle buttplate and is drilled and tapped for an optional tang sight. The **Deluxe Sporter** model (30″ barrel) has a shotgun butt, pistol grip, and traditional cheek rest.

Other round-barreled versions of the Model 1874 include the **Carbine** with 24″ barrel, the **Business Rifle** with 28″ heavy tapered barrel, and the **Military** model with its 30″ barrel.

New Model 1875 Breech Loading Metallic Cartridge Rifles
Type: Breech loading
Caliber: .40-50 to .45-120, .22RF, and .32-40, .38-55 Win & Ballard
Barrel Length: 24″, 26″, and 30″
Weight: 7.38 lbs to 9.25 lbs
Length: 41″ to 47″ overall
Stock: American walnut
C Sharps Arms offers their **New Model 1875** in **Sporting, Saddle,** and **Carbine** variations. All three are for metallic cartridges, 14″ pull, single trigger, blade front sight, buckhorn rear barrel sight and a straight grip

buttstock. The **Sporting** and **Saddle** rifles both have standard tapered octagonal barrels (30″ and 26″ respectively) and the **Carbine** model has a round 24″ barrel.

Springfield Armory, Inc

M1 Garand
Type: Semi-automatic, gas operated, clip fed
Caliber: .30-06 Springfield or optional .308 or .270
Barrel Length: 24″ Standard and Sniper; 18.25″ Tanker

Opposite, bottom: The Savage Model 110, modified for metallic silhouette target shooting. *This page, in descending order:* The C Sharps Long Range Express Rifle is based on a model of truly legendary long range accuracy: the New Model 1875 Carbine sports a 'newfangled' round barrel; and the New Model 1875 Saddle Rifle has a tapered octagonal barrel and buckhorn rear sight. Springfield Armory duplicates the famous M-1 Garand in its various configurations. Shown *below* is the M-1 Standard model with a commercial scope and *above* is the M1-D Sniper Rifle.

Overleaf: In this historic photograph, troopers of the Indian-fighting US Army 13th Cavalry pose with their Springfield Model 1873 rifles, which were Army standard issue from 1872-94. *Note* the .45-70 ammo in their bullet belts.

Weight: 9.5 lbs

Length: 43″ overall Standard and Sniper; 37.5″ overall Tanker

Stock: Walnut

Sights: Blade with protecting ears front; aperture rear

Magazine Capacity: 8 round en-bloc clip

John Garand's M1 Rifle was standard issue to US combat troops during most of WWII and the Korean Conflict. Referred to by General George S Patton as 'the greatest battle implement ever devised,' Springfield Armory is again manufacturing an exact duplicate of the classic M1. Today's **M1 Garand** comes in 3 different models with a wide range of historical and accurizing accessories.

The **Standard, National Match,** and **Ultra Match** models sport a two stage, 5 lb trigger pull. Match models also feature special match barrels, sights and glass-bedded stocks. The **'Tanker' Garand** is a lighter weight, short-barreled version with a modified handguard, special main spring and follower rod. In addition to walnut, the Tanker model is also available in folding stock. Other features are as per the Standard M1 model.

The **M1-D Sniper** is an exact duplicate of the **M1 Sniper** rifle utilized during the Korean War. It combines standard M1 features with a special sniper barrel, authentic **M84** scopes and scope mounts, prong type flash suppressors, leather sniper cheek pads, and leather slings.

M1A (Military Designation: M14)

Type: Rotating bolt, gas operated, semi-automatic, air cooled, magazine fed

Caliber: 7.62mm/.308

Barrel Length: 22″ Standard and Match; 18½″ Bush

Weight: 8.98 lbs Standard and National Match; 9 lbs 15 oz Super Match; 8.75 lbs Bush

Length: 44.5″ overall Standard and Match; 40.5″ walnut stock, 27.5″ to 38″ extendable Bush.

Stock: Walnut or fiberglass Standard; glass-bedded, oil finished Match; walnut or folding paratrooper Bush

Sights: Military square post front; military aperture rear.

Magazine Capacity: 5, 10, 20, or 25-round box type

The Springfield Armory **M1A** is the civilian version of the **M14,** designed and engineered to precise military specifications. Available in **Standard, Match,** and **Bush Rifle** models, the full range of accessories allows for optimum stylization. Standard model features include a sight radius of 21.06″, trigger pull of 4.5–7.5 lbs and a maximum range of 4103 yards.

The **National Match** and **Super Match M1As** are hand-assembled with National Match barrel, sights, main spring guide,

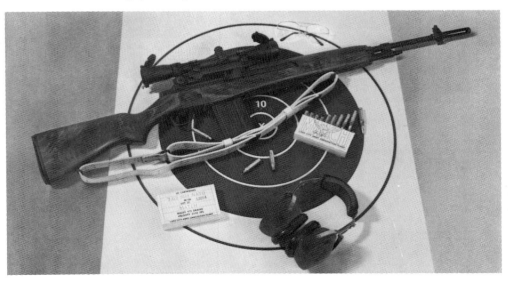

Springfield Armory's M-1 Garand *(above opposite, immediate left and above)* comes complete with various historic and accurizing accessories. The M-1 was US military standard issue in World War II and Korea. The Springfield M6 Scout *(top of page)* is a single shot .22/.410 over-and-under which can store 15 .22s and 4 .410s in its detachable stock. The Springfield M1A *(far left)* is the civilian version of the M14, has a maximum range of 4103 yards and has a wide range of accessories for optimum stylization.

flash suppressor, and gas cylinder. The Super Match model also sports an air-gauged heavy barrel and modified op rod guide. Both have a 4.5 lb trigger pull with most other specs identical to the Standard M1A. The **M1A-A1 Bush** is a lightweight and compact rifle designed for law enforcement and military applications. It has a sight radius of 22″ and accepts all M1A parts and accessories. Other specs are per Standard M1A except as noted.

M6 Scout

Caliber: .22 LR/.410 shotgun; .22 Magnum; .22 Hornet
Barrel Length: 18″
Weight: 4 lbs
Length: 31.5″ overall
Stock: Folding stock that completely disassembles from the barrel group with removable pivot pin
Sights: Military aperture for .22; v-notch for .410
Magazine Capacity: Single shot, with 15 (.22) or 4 (.410) stored in stock

Based on the original military design of the US Air Force M6 Survival Rifle, the **M6 Scout** is lightweight, compact, and versatile. Standard features include a push-pull selector knob on the hammer that makes the switch from .22 rifle to .410 shotgun. The M6 Scout also features a special trigger bar, cross-bolt safety, and sight radius of 16.13″.

Sturm, Ruger & Company, Inc

Ruger M-77 Bolt Action Rifles

Type: Bolt action, centerfire
Caliber: In 14 calibers including .270, .338 Win Mag, .220 Swift
Barrel Length: 18.5″ (Model M-77RSI) to 26″ (Model M-77V)
Weight: 6 lbs to 9 lbs
Stock: American walnut

Available in a total of six model configurations, all **M-77s** feature an external bolt stop, heat-treated steel barrels, receivers and bolts, two massive front locking lugs and a positive long extractor combined with one-piece bolt construction. The trigger action is smooth and free from creep at all adjustments; the safety, securely mounted in the heavy metal of the tang, is positive, readily accessible, and of the shotgun type. The basic Ruger **M-77R** has an integral base receiver, 1″ scope rings, weighs approximately 7 lbs and is offered in both short stroke and Magnum action lengths in a broad selection of calibers. Model **M-77RS** takes

the basic model and adds open sights to the standard features in barrel lengths of 22″ and 24″. The **M-77V Varmint** model is Ruger's heavyweight 9 lb Bolt Action Rifle, available with either heavy 24″ barrel in calibers .22-250, 6mm, .243, .25-06, and .308 or a 26″ barrel in .220 Swift caliber.

Ruger's model **M-77RSI International** bolt action rifle has as its special features full length forearm stock, integral base receiver, open sights, and Ruger 1″ steel rings. Available in Magnum action calibers .270 and .30-06 and short-stoke action calibers .22-250, .250-3000, .243 and .308, all versions sport 18.5″ barrels and weigh approximately

The gas-operated semi-automatic Springfield M1A 7.62mm/.308 Caliber Rifle is shown *at left* in its Super Match configuration—hand-assembled with National Match sights, main spring guide, flash suppressor, gas canister and air-gauged heavy barrel—all improvements to an already highly accurate and reliable design. The rifle is shown *here* with the optional burly walnut stock, 3 × 9 scope and leather sling. The very elegant Ruger 77/22 Rimfire Rifle *(below)* features the patented Ruger 10-shot rotary magazine, has a solid component receiver and is made of heat-treated steel—a happy blend of Ruger M-77 model and Ruger 10/22 characteristics. The 77/22 has no iron sights but is set up with Ruger scope rings—the scope is not included. *At bottom, below* are two views of the Ruger M-77's bolt action: *at left*—visible *opposite the bolt handle* is the M-77's bolt stop—and *at right,* the hand checkering on the stock's pistol grip.

7 lbs. Common to all M-77s, the International model also has a pistol grip and forearm that are hand checkered in a sharp diamond pattern.

Equipped with open sights, a 24″ barrel and .458 Win Mag caliber only, the 8.75 lb Ruger **M-77RS-Tropical** has a steel trigger guard and floor plate. The Ruger **M-77RL Ultra Light** completes the line in just 6 lbs with both long and short action versions, an integral base receiver and 1″ scope rings. The Ultra Light big game rifle is available with both Magnum and short stroke actions, all with a 20″ barrel.

Ruger No 1 Single-Shot Rifles
Type: Single-shot, centerfire
Caliber: Various
Barrel Length: 20″ to 26″
Weight: 7.25 lbs to 9 lbs
Stock: American walnut

The Ruger **No 1** falling block rifle combines modern engineering with a finely finished and closely fitted mechanism. The heart of the design is the massive receiver which handles any type of modern cartridge case and the sliding shotgun-type safety engages both the sear and hammer directly to provide maximum security. The **No 1 Standard** has

a 26″ barrel, semi-beavertail forearm, and quarter rib with 1″ scope rings. Available in 15 different calibers from .22-250 to .338 Win Mag, the standard rifle weighs in at 8 lbs.

Produced in a variety of popular calibers suitable for small, medium, and large game, the **No 1 Light Sporter**, **No 1 Medium Sporter** and **No 1 Tropical** models each have an adjustable folding leaf rear sight base and dovetail type gold bead front sight. The Light Sporter has a lightweight 22″ barrel; the Medium Sporter has a medium 26″ barrel; the Tropical sports a 24″ heavy

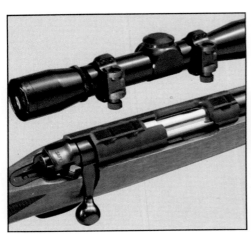

barrel and with .458 Win Mag caliber weighs in at 9 lbs overall.

Ruger's **No 1 International** features a lightweight 20″ barrel, full length forearm, and in 7.25 lbs offers an adjustable folding rear sight and ramp front sight base with dovetail type gold bead. The **No 1 Special Varminter** has a semi-beavertail forearm, a heavy 24″ barrel tapped for target scope block and 1″ Ruger scope rings.

Ruger 77/22 Rimfire Rifles

Type: Bolt action, rimfire
Caliber: .22 LR
Barrel Length: 20″
Weight: 5.75 lbs
Length: 39.25″ overall
Stock: American walnut
Magazine Capacity: 10-shot Ruger rotary

The Ruger .22 caliber rimfire bolt action rifle was conceived as an elegant small game and target rifle. Blending the characteristics of the Ruger M-77 with the Ruger 10/22 semi-automatic rimfire rifle, Sturm Ruger has produced a smallbore sporting rifle made of heat treated steel, a solid component receiver, and the patented Ruger 10-shot rotary magazine.

Plain barrel **Model 77/22R** has no iron sights but does have 1″ Ruger scope rings. **Model 77/22RS** incorporates iron sights with the 1″ scope rings, and **Model 77/22S** has both a gold bead front sight and folding leaf rear sight. All versions of the 77/22 rimfire possess Ruger's three-position safety that, in its rearmost position, locks the bolt closed.

Ruger Mini-14 Semi-Automatic Rifles

Type: Rotating bolt semi-automatic
Caliber: .223
Weight: 6.5 lbs (full stock) to 7.76 lbs (folding stock)

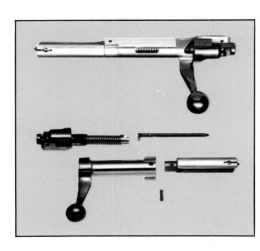

Clockwise, from immediate left: One of 21 special edition Ruger North Americans—Ruger No 1 Single-Shot Rifles, each bearing a gold-inlay, presentation-grade engraving of a North American game animal; the Ruger Scope Mounting System; the Ruger M-77RL Ultra Light Bolt Action Rifle; the M-77RS Tropical, in .458 Winchester Magnum; the M-77RSI International with 18.5″ barrel; the basic M-77, offered with either a 'short stroke' or Magnum action; the Ruger No 1 Light Sporter (shown), a great single-shot rifle; the No 1 International with a 20″ barrel; the No 1 Special Varminter, with heavy 24″ barrel; the No 1 Standard Rifle, available in calibers ranging from .22-250 to .338 Winchester Magnum; and the Ruger 77/22 Rimfire Rifle bolt, with view of its disassembly.

From the top: The Ruger .223 caliber Mini-14 Ranch Rifle with solid stock; the K-Mini-14/5F with folding stock; and the K-Mini-14 in stainless steel. The Ruger Model 10/22 Autoloading Carbines are available in both Deluxe Sporter *(bottom)* and Standard *(below)* models.

Length: 37.25″ overall full stock; 27.5″ to 37.75″ overall folding stock
Stock: American hardwood
Magazine Capacity: 5 rounds

The **Mini-14 Semi-Automatic Rifle** is rugged, easy to handle, lightweight, and consists of relatively few components. The mechanism employs the Ruger fixed piston/moving cylinder gas system in conjunction with a simplified Garand-type rotating bolt. It has a ventilated fiberglass handguard to protect the shooter's hand from barrel heat and the moving slide and can be field-stripped to its basic subassemblies in seconds without the use of tools.

The basic Mini-14 Semi-Automatic is offered in two full length stock models, the **Mini-14/5** with blued finish and **K-Mini-14/5** with stainless steel components. In a folding stock the available models are the **Mini-14/5F** with blued finish and the **K-Mini-14/5F** with stainless steel components.

The **Mini-14 Ranch Rifle** is designed for use with telescopic sights, incorporating a low, compact mounting feature for comfortable scope use and convenience in carrying. It features a unique buffer system that redirects and absorbs recoil shock and a redesigned bolt ejector system. Chambered for the same .223 cartridge, the Mini-14 Ranch Rifle is available in a full length stock models **Mini-14/5R** with blued finish and **K-Mini-14/5R** with stainless steel components, and in a stainless steel compact folding system model, **K-Mini-14/5RF**.

Available for shipment only to excise tax exempt agencies and to sworn officers who are authorized to use this equipment, Sturm Ruger also produces a 20-round **Mini-14/20 GB Government** model. The Government Model has the same basic features of the Mini-14 incorporated with a muzzle flash hider, military bayonet stud type protected front sight, and heat-resistant, ventilated fiberglass handguard.

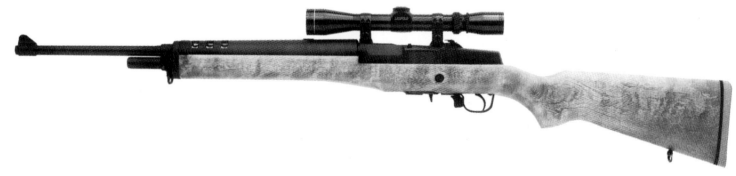

The Ruger AC-556 Automatic Rifle *(above)* is capable of semi-automatic, 3-shot burst and full automatic (750rpm) operation. *Left:* The Ruger AC-556F has a folding stock. *Below:* The Ruger XGI autoloader and *(at bottom)* its improved Garand-type rotating bolt mechanism.

Ruger Model 10/22 Autoloading Carbine
Type: Rimfire autoloader
Caliber: .22 LR
Barrel Length: 18.5″
Weight: 5 lbs
Length: 37.25″ overall
Stock: American hardwood; walnut (Deluxe model)
Magazine Capacity: 10 rounds
The Ruger **10/22** is a combination of light weight, short overall length, and mechanical dependability. Its trigger housing contains the entire ignition mechanism which employs a high speed swinging hammer to en-sure short lock-time. The **Standard Carbine Model 10/22RB** has stocks of American hardwood; the **Deluxe Sporter Model 10/22DSP** has hand checkered American walnut stocks and sling swivels.

Ruger Selective Fire AC-556 Automatic Rifles
Type: Automatic
Caliber: .223
Barrel Length: 18.5″; 13″ (folding stock)
Weight: 6.5 lbs
Length: 37.25″ overall (full stock); 23.75″ to 33.5″ overall (folding stock)
Stock: American hardwood
Magazine Capacity: 30 rounds
The **Ruger AC-556** automatic rifle, avail-able for shipment to excise tax exempt agencies only, is equipped with a reinforced one-piece American hardwood stock and heat-resistant, ventilated fiberglass handguard, muzzle flash hider and military bayonet stud type protected front sight. With a cyclic rate of fire of 750 RPM, this Selective Fire rifle comes with either fully automatic fire, 3-shot burst, or semi-automatic operation.
Also available with steel folding stock, the **Ruger AC-556F** automatic rifle design is

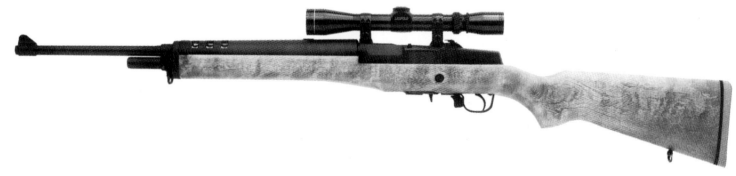

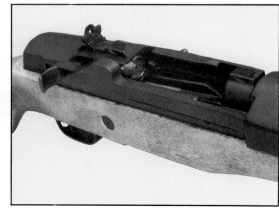

best adapted for aircraft and helicopter operations, patrol vehicles, dignitary protection, and any other application where a high rate of accurate fire must be combined with compactness and short overall length.

Ruger XGI Semi-Automatic Rifle

Type: Semi-automatic
Caliber: .243 Win, .308 Win
Barrel Length: 20″
Weight: 8 lbs
Length: 39.88″ overall
Stock: American hardwood
Magazine Capacity: 5 rounds

Chambered for two of the most popular varmint-to-deer and big game sporting rounds, the Ruger **XGI** is similar in design and operation to the Ruger Mini-14 but is longer and more powerful. Its mechanism employs a Garand-type, two lug rotating bolt which offers 50% more shear area than the M14, and music wire coil springs are used throughout to give reliability under adverse operating conditions. The XGI has a rugged blade front sight on an integral ramp and an auxiliary folding peep rear sight, adjustable for windage and elevation.

Thompson/Center Arms

Cherokee Percussion Sporting Rifle

Type: Single shot muzzleloader
Caliber: .32 and .45
Barrel Length: 24″
Weight: 6 lbs
Stock: American walnut

A lightweight percussion sporting rifle, Thompson/Center Arms' **Cherokee** muzzleloader features interchangeable accessory barrels to allow the user to hunt everything from squirrel to deer with the same rifle. The Cherokee has a hooked breech system, colored cased lock contoured with a dolphin-shaped hammer, and open hunting style sights that are adjustable for windage and elevation both.

Contender Carbine

Type: Single shot
Caliber: 8 rifle calibers; .410 gauge shotgun
Barrel Length: 21″
Stock: American walnut

The **Contender Carbine** is a strong, accurate single shot firearm stocked with American walnut, handcheckered, and completed with a rubber recoil pad. All barrels are 21″, blued, have adjustable iron sights and are tapped and drilled for scope mounts. The .410 shotshell barrels are full choke, chambered for 3″ shells, and feature a raised ventilated rib.

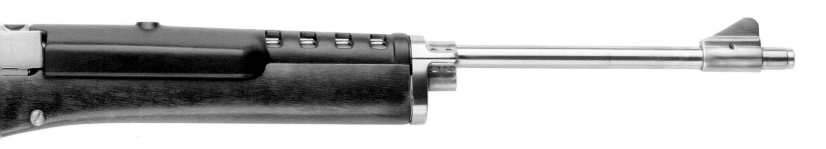

Hawken Muzzleloading Sporting Rifle
Type: Single shot muzzleloader
Caliber: .45, .50, and .54
Barrel Length: 28"
Weight: 8.5 lbs
Stock: American walnut

Thompson/Center Arms' **Hawken Muzzle-loader** is intended for 'serious shooting' and modeled after the famous Rocky Mountain rifles made during the 1800s. It features a hooked breech, double set triggers, adjustable hunting sights, and solid brass trim. A presentation quality **Hawken Cougar** features the best of Thompson/Center's select walnut stock, stainless steel fittings, and a crouched cougar medallion to identify it as a unique Hawken Cougar. The Cougar model is available in cap lock .45 and .50 calibers only.

Renegade Muzzleloading Rifle
Type: Single shot muzzleloader
Caliber: .50 and .54 percussion or .50 flint
Barrel Length: 26"
Weight: 8 lbs
Stock: American walnut

Thompson/Center's **Renegade Muzzleloader** is constructed from superior modern steel with investment cast parts fitted to a fine grain American walnut stock. With its .50 and .54 caliber power, T/C touts the Renegade as having workhorse reliability backed by a lifetime warranty. It features a hooked breech system, coil spring lock, double set triggers, adjustable hunting sights and steel trim. A second variation, the **Renegade .56 Caliber Musket** has a 26" barrel bored smooth from breech to muzzle.

Seneca Muzzleloading Rifle
Type: Single shot muzzleloader
Caliber: .36 and .45
Barrel Length: 27"
Weight: 6 lbs
Stock: American walnut

Patterned on the style of an early New England hunting rifle, T/C's **Seneca .45 Cal**

The Ruger K-Mini-14/5RF Ranch Rifle *(at top)* in stainless steel has a folding stock and (like all Ruger Ranch Rifles) a patented recoil shock buffer system for telescopic sights. The Thompson/Center Arms Cherokee Percussion Sporting Rifle *(mid-page)* has interchangeable accessory barrels in .32 and .45 calibers to provide a wide range of hunting possibilities, and its sights are windage- and elevation-adjustable. Thompson/Center's Contender Carbine *(above left)* is an elegant, strong and accurate single-shot, available in 8 rifle calibers as well as .410 (3" shotshells). The Contender has adjustable iron sights, and its 21" barrel is tapped and drilled for scope mounts.

In descending order from the top of this page : Thompson/Center Arms' big bore Hawken Muzzleloading Sporting Rifle is available in .45, .50 and .54 calibers and has adjustable hunting sights. TCR's Renegade muzzleloader is made of modern steel, has 'workhorse reliability' and a lifetime guarantee.

Thompson/Center Arms' Seneca is patterned after an early New England hunting rifle and has fully adjustable triggers and sights. Among TCR's cartridge-firing Single Shot Rifles, the Hunter Field model features an adjustable trigger and interchangeable barrels for firing a variety of cartridges.

Percussion Muzzleloader is best suited for hunting deer size game and the .36 for squirrels, turkey, and other small game. The barrel is precision rifled, polished and blued to a high luster finish and the Seneca has a hooked breech system. Fully adjustable triggers and hunting style sights adjustable for windage and elevation complete this muzzleloader's standard features.

TCR '83 Single Shot Rifles
Caliber: .22 Hornet; .222, .223, .22/250 Rem; .243, .270, .308 Win; 7mm Rem Mag; .30/06 Springfield

Barrel Length: 23″
Weight: 6.88 lbs
Length: 39.5″ overall
Stock: American black walnut
Common to both Thompson/Center **Single Shot Rifles** are their break-open design with top lever; completely interchangeable barrels, tapped and drilled for scope mounts; ramp front sight and adjustable, folding rear sight; and a cross bolt safety with secondary lock.

The **Hunter Field** model features a buttstock and forend with pistol grip and a stainless steel adjustable single trigger with double

lever advantage. The **Aristocrat** model has stainless steel adjustable 'double set' triggers which function either as double set or single stage. Its black walnut stock has a cheek piece on the left side of the buttstock. A rubber recoil pad comes with both models.

Ultra Light Arms, Inc

Ultralight 'Ultimate Mountain' Rifles
Type: Bolt action
Caliber: various, 21 in all
Barrel Length: 22″ (Models 20 and 24); 24″ Model 28

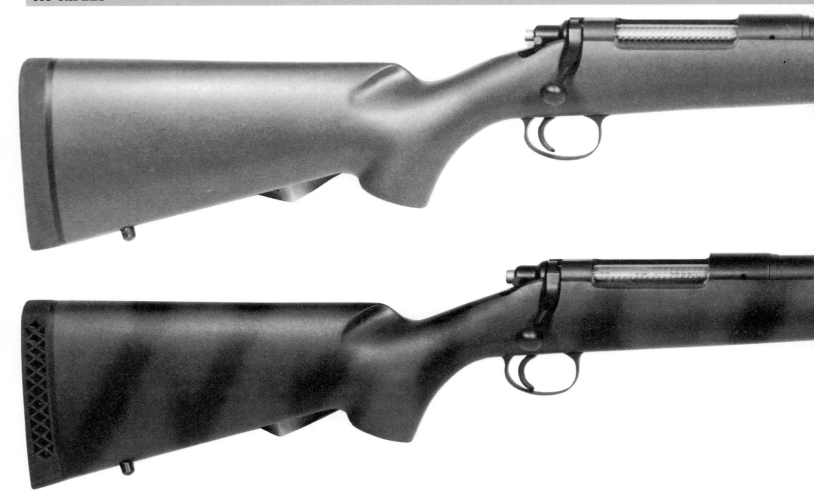

Weight: 4.5 lbs to 5.5 lbs
Stock: Kevlar/graphite combination
Ultra Light has combined aerospace technology with gunsmithing to produce rifles that weigh significantly less than other full size competitors. The stock is composed of Kevlar and graphite in a classic style and incorporates an integrally cast recoil area, recoil pad and reinforced swivel studs. They feature Douglas premium barrels and Timney triggers, the only two parts not manufactured by Ultra Light. Ultra Light receivers are machined from ordnance grade heat treated steel, have a 3″ magazine capacity, and are available either right- or left-handed.

Model 20 with its 22″ barrel is available in calibers .22-250 Rem .243 Win, 6mm Rem., .257 Roberts, 7x57, 7mm 08 Rem, .284 Win, and .308 Win as standards. Improved and other calibers are available on request. A Model 20 Left Hand is also offered with all specs matching those of Model 20 except for its mirror image left-hand action and stock.
Model 24 incorporates all the standard series features with calibers of .25-06 Rem, .270 Win, .280 Rem, and .30-06. Other calibers may be provided on request as will the left handed version of the Model 24.
Model 28 features a 24″ Douglas premium no. 2 contour barrel and is 45″ overall in

length. It is chambered for .264 Win, 7mm Rem Mag, .300 Win Mag, and .338 Win Mag Including either a KDF or Ultra Light Arms recoil arrestor, any other custom feature or caliber may be built in to this rifle.

US Repeating Arms Company

Winchester Model 70 Bolt Action Centerfire Rifles
Type: Bolt action, centerfire
Barrel Length: 20″ to 24″
Weight: 5.75 lbs to 8.5 lbs
Length: 39″ to 44.5″ overall

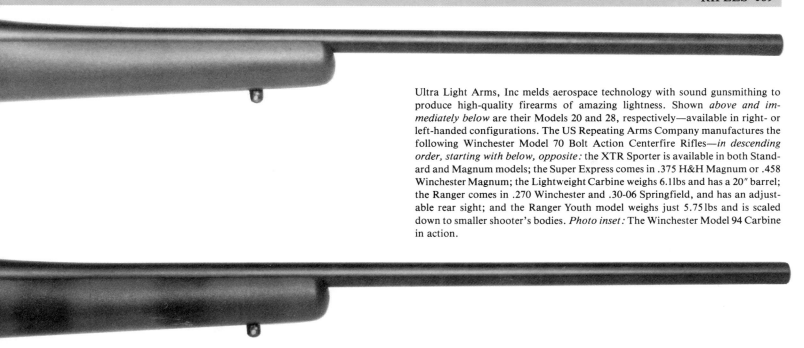

Ultra Light Arms, Inc melds aerospace technology with sound gunsmithing to produce high-quality firearms of amazing lightness. Shown *above and immediately below* are their Models 20 and 28, respectively—available in right- or left-handed configurations. The US Repeating Arms Company manufactures the following Winchester Model 70 Bolt Action Centerfire Rifles—*in descending order, starting with below, opposite:* the XTR Sporter is available in both Standard and Magnum models; the Super Express comes in .375 H&H Magnum or .458 Winchester Magnum; the Lightweight Carbine weighs 6.1lbs and has a 20" barrel; the Ranger comes in .270 Winchester and .30-06 Springfield, and has an adjustable rear sight; and the Ranger Youth model weighs just 5.75lbs and is scaled down to smaller shooter's bodies. *Photo inset:* The Winchester Model 94 Carbine in action.

Stock: Walnut

Magazine Capacity: 3 to 5 rounds

As a result of having been in continuous production and development for close to 50 years, the Winchester **Model 70** has taken advantage of many refinements and technological advancements. The **Model 70 XTR Sporter Rifle** series offers calibers .25-06 Rem, .270 Win, .30-06 Springfield, and .308 Win in a **Standard** model, all with Monte Carlo stock and cheekpiece, a hinged steel floorplate, jeweled bolt, detachable sling swivels, rifle sights, and a 24" barrel. In its **Magnum** version, the same sporter features and 24" barrel are combined with 7mm Rem Mag and Win Mag calibers .264, .300, and .338. In three flat-shooting calibers designed for small game, a special **Var-**mint model has a 24" high-strength Winchester steel barrel without sights. The **Model XTR Super Express Rifle** comes in two big-game calibers (.375 H&H Mag or .458 Win Mag) and has the Sporter stock reinforced with two steel crossbolts, a forward sling swivel, and adjustable open rear and ramp front sights.

In its **Featherweight** version, the Model 70 XTR is offered in .270 Win and .30-06 Springfield calibers. The Featherweight has a 22" barrel, weights 6.75 lbs, and has a receiver drilled and tapped for scope mounting. A special European version of the Featherweight combines the same features with a 6.5x55 Swedish Mauser caliber. In addition, a limited edition .270 Win **Ultra Grade Featherweight** with 24 karat gold hand engraving and custom hand fitting is available, serial numbered 1 to 1000.

Winchester's **Model 70 Lightweight Carbine** is available in six calibers: .22-250 and .223 Rem, .243, .270 and .308 Win, and .30-06 Springfield. A light and fast handling

utility and brush gun, this carbine is a compact 6 lbs with a 20″ barrel. The Winchester **Ranger Bolt Action Rifle** comes in .270 Win and .30-06 Springfield calibers, has ramped bead front and adjustable rear sights, and a one-piece American hardwood stock. In .243 Win caliber, the **Ranger Youth Bolt Action Carbine** is size-scaled to fit younger or smaller shooters, weighs 5.75 lbs, has ramped bead front and semi-buckhorn folding leaf rear sights, and is composed of American hardwood stock.

Winchester's **Model 70 Winlite** offers the Model 70 bolt action in a fiberglass stock for light weight, strength, accuracy, and ulimate stability for bedding of the barreled action. Available in four calibers and in barrel lengths of 22″ and 24″, stocks have a contoured rubber recoil pad and sling swivel studs.

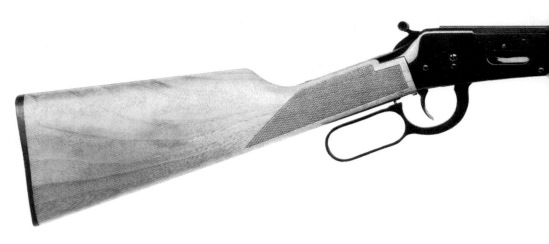

Winchester Model 94 Carbines

Type: Lever action, centerfire
Barrel Length: 16″ to 24″
Weight: 6 lbs to 7 lbs
Length: 33.75″ to 41.75″ overall
Stock: American walnut
Magazine Capacity: 5 to 9 rounds

As a hunting rifle, US Repeating Arms claims that the Winchester **Model 94** has earned the reputation of 'the lever action legend.' They are made with forged steel receivers designed for side ejection of spent cartridges and top mounting of scopes and each carbine comes packaged with a thumb hammer extension reversible for right or left handed use with a scope.

In the **Model 94 XTR Carbine**, the .30-30 caliber combined with a 20″ barrel, dovetailed blade front and semi-buckhorn rear sights, a six-round capacity magazine cartridge, precise cut checkering and butt plate. The **XTR in 7-30 Waters**, developed for higher muzzle velocity and flatter-shooting accuracy, features a 24″ barrel with a dovetailed blade front sight and seven cartridge capacity.

Winchester's **Model 94 Standard Carbine** is available in .30-30 Win with a six-shot magazine, 20″ steel barrel, composition butt plate, and dovetailed blade front and adjustable rear sights. The compact **Trapper Carbine** combines a 16″ barrel with post front sight with either a five-shot magazine .30-30 Win or .45 Colt and .44 Rem Mag calibers with nine-cartridge capacity. The **Winchester Range Lever Action Carbine** in a five-

Winchester's legendary Model 94 Carbines, *from left to the bottom of the page:* the .30-30 caliber XTR; the 7-30 Waters XTR; the 94 Standard; the 16″ barrel, big bore Trapper; and the Ranger in .30-06 Springfield. *Below:* John Wayne poses with an antique Winchester carbine.

Top left: The Chief Crazy Horse Model 94 Winchester celebrates the great Sioux chief and his people, is beautifully and symbolically engraved and is chambered for the classic 38-55 Winchester cartridge. *Left:* The Annie Oakley Commemorative Model 9422 Rifle—a highly decorative .22 caliber lever action. *Above:* The beautifully and informatively engraved Winchester/Colt Commemorative set combines two legends of the Wild West. *Note* Oliver Winchester's likeness on the rifle's receiver.

shot .30-30 Win caliber offers economy in American hardwood stock with a 20″ barrel and blade front, semi-buckhorn rear sights. The **Model 94 Big Bore** lever action carbine

for North American big game utilizes .375, .356 or .307 Win cartridges. Featuring side ejection, Monte Carlo stocks of American walnut, sling swivels, and a reversible thumb hammer extension, the receiver is forged steel with reinforced side panels and has been drilled and tapped for top mounting of scopes. Lastly, to celebrate the Winchester 120th Anniversary, limited edition Model 94 carbines commemorating founder Oliver F Winchester, the horse-and-rider trademark, and Chief Crazy Horse are available in highly decorative versions.

Winchester Model 9422 Rifles

Type: Lever action, rimfire
Caliber: .22 S, L, LR and .22 WMR
Barrel Length: 20.5″ and 22.2″
Weight: 6.25 lbs and 6.5 lbs
Length: 37.13″ and 39.13″ overall
Stock: American walnut
Magazine Capacity: 11 to 21 rounds

Ranked among the world's finest production sporting arms, **Model 9422 XTR Rifles** feature positive lever action and bolt design for feeding and chambering from any shooting position. The receiver, frame, and finger

US Repeating Arms' Winchester Commemorative Models are all limited edition firearms, featuring the handsome Winchester engraving, which, in commemorative models, is designed around historical images and tastefully calligraphed lettering. Insofar as the Annie Oakley is the first US firearm to commemorate an historic woman, the Boy Scout Commemorative Model 9422—*shown at far right,* complete with commemorative .22 Long ammunition—may well claim to be the first such honor for that organization. *Below:* The Winchester Model 9422 Standard with 20.5″ barrel; ramp bead front and semi-buckhorn rear sights; and adjustable thumb-hammer extension for right- or left-handed shooting. *Above:* Weaver Arms, Ltd's Nighthawk semi-automatic carbine combines nylon, aluminum and steel in a rugged, high-quality 9mm firearm.

lever are forged steel, receivers are designed for side ejection of spent cartridges and grooved for top mounting of scopes. Each rifle has an adjustable thumb hammer extension, exposed hammer with half-cock safety, ramped bead front sight and semi-buckhorn rear sight.

The **Standard Model 9422 XTR Rifle** has a western saddle carbine profile with a straight stock and forearm with barrel band, traditional finger lever and composition butt plate. **Model 9422 XTR Classic Rifle** features include a satin-finished walnut stock with fluted comb and crescent steel butt plate, curved finger lever and undercut pistol grip and an extended forearm with barrel band and 22.5″ barrel for longer-range accuracy.

Model 9422 Commemoratives include a maximum 15,000 units of a **'Boy Scouts of America' Rifle** and 6000 units of an **'Annie Oakley' Rifle,** each offered in a highly decorative presentation format.

Weaver Arms, Ltd

Nighthawk
Type: Semi-automatic carbine
Caliber: 9mm
Barrel Length: 16.1″
Weight: 6.5 lbs
Length: 26.5″ to 33.5″ overall (with stock retracted and extended)

Finish: Black
Magazine Capacity: 25 or 32 rounds
Weaver Arms' **Nighthawk** fires from a closed bolt and features stainless steel internal working parts including the safety levers and trigger. Its upper receiver, top cover and stock rod guides are aluminum extrusions and the barrel, produced by ER Shaw of Pennsylvania, is of the highest quality steel. Gun composition is completed with 30% fiberglass filled nylon grip sights, cocking knob and lower receiver.

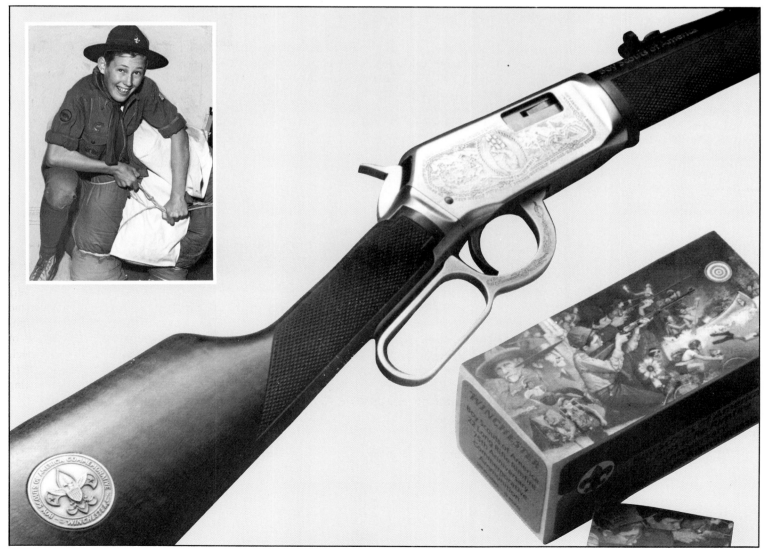

MACHINE AND SUBMACHINE GUNS

Auto-Ordnance Corporation

Thompson 1927A-1, A-3
Type: Semi-automatic carbine
Caliber: .45 (A-1 models), .22 (A-3 model)
Barrel Length: 16″
Weight: 11.5 lbs
Stock: Walnut
Sights: Standard military (Standard A-1 and A-3 models); Deluxe rear sight and compensator (Deluxe and Lightweight A-1 models)
Magazine Capacity: 15, 20, 30 rounds (A-1 models), 10, 30 rounds (A-3)

All versions of this Thompson classic have frames and receivers of solid milled steel with burnished metal parts. The **Standard** model has a plain barrel and horizontal military forearm made popular by the World War II version that was carried by Allied Forces. The modern **Deluxe** and **Lightweight** models feature a finger-grooved vertical foregrip, finned barrel, and adjustable rear sight and compensator. The **Lightweight (1C)** model is identical in appearance to the Deluxe but manufactured in a lightweight alloy that reduces its overall weight by 20%.

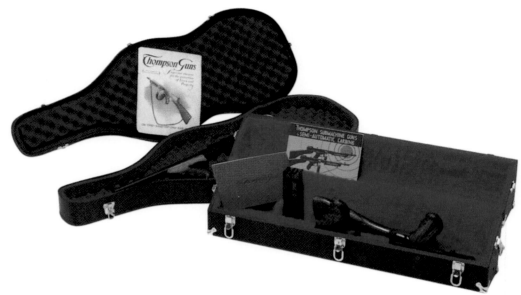

This lightweight alloy version of the **1927A-3** combines classic features with the economy of a .22 caliber design. All other features are those of the Deluxe model, with finned barrel, compensator, and walnut stocks and grips.

Thompson 1927M-1 Military Assault Rifle
Type: Semi-automatic and fully-automatic
Caliber: .45
Barrel Length: 16″
Weight: 11.5 lbs

The Auto-Ordnance Thompson 1927 A-1 semi-automatic carbine *(left)* and the full- or semi-automatic 1927 M-1 Military Assault Rifle *(see box above)* are revivals of the originals in all but those design characteristics which have been modified to comply with contemporary firearms legislation. The A-1 is made of solid milled steel and burnished metal parts. Auto-Ordnance also makes a lightweight model—the 1C—having the same appearance but made of lightweight alloys. Both the A-1 and M1 are .45 caliber and saw extensive World War II service in the hands of US Army soldiers. Which side are you on? *Above left:* Auto-Ordnance makes a classic Roaring Twenties gangster-style 'violin case' for Thompsons, as well as a more staid FBI-style hard case; both provide space for extra clips and drum magazines, as well as handsome protection for your 'Tommygun.' Top of page: Wire spoke wheel, ballooning fender and a Thompson combine to evoke another bygone chapter in American folk history.

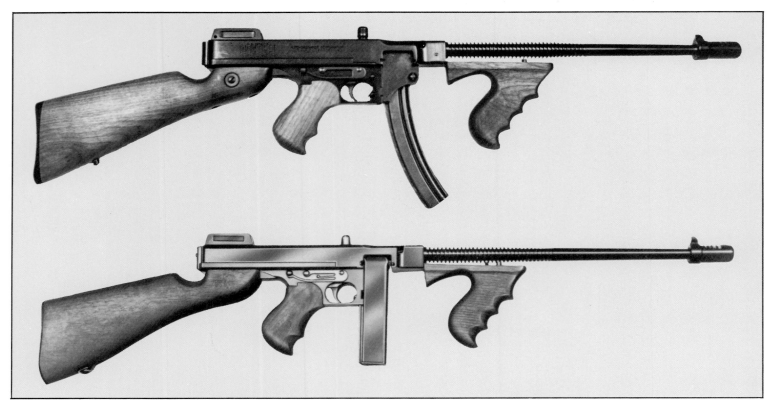

Above: The Thompson .22 caliber 1927 A-3 semi-automatic, on classic display. *Note* its 30-round 'banana' clip. *Below:* The Thompson M-1, with some of its buddies of bygone years. The submachine gun is .45 caliber. *Above left, top:* The 1928 Full Auto, with banana clip and *(below it)* the A-1 Deluxe with straight clip. *Left:* Marines armed with Thompsons, an M1 Garand *(left, center)* and a Browning Automatic Rifle *(right, center)* police a Chinese town in late 1945.

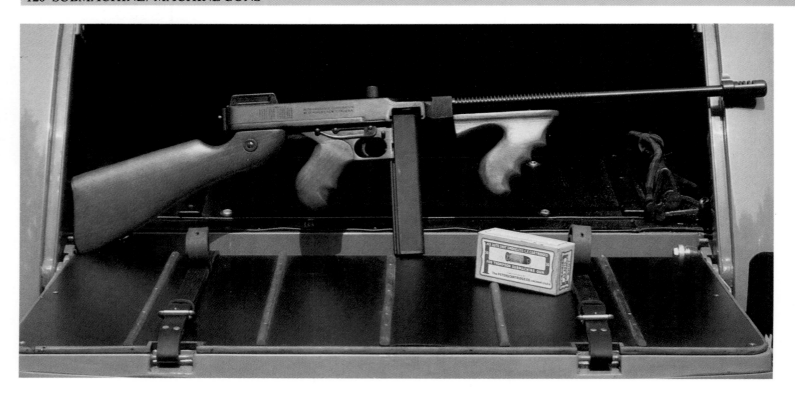

Stock: Walnut
Sights: Standard military
The original Thompson **M-1,** used throughout world battles, is a legendary military firearm. Authentic down to the side cocking lever, the current production of the Thompson M-1 duplicates this first and most famous military assault rifle. Its frame and receiver are milled from solid steel with a finish of special military flat back.

Thompson 1928 Full Auto
Type: Fully automatic
Barrel Length: 10.5″
Stock: Walnut
After more than a half century, the **1928 Thompson submachine gun** is still in production. This fully automatic weapon is crafted with a vertical foregrip, finned 10.5″ barrel and compensator. Metal parts are burnished blue.

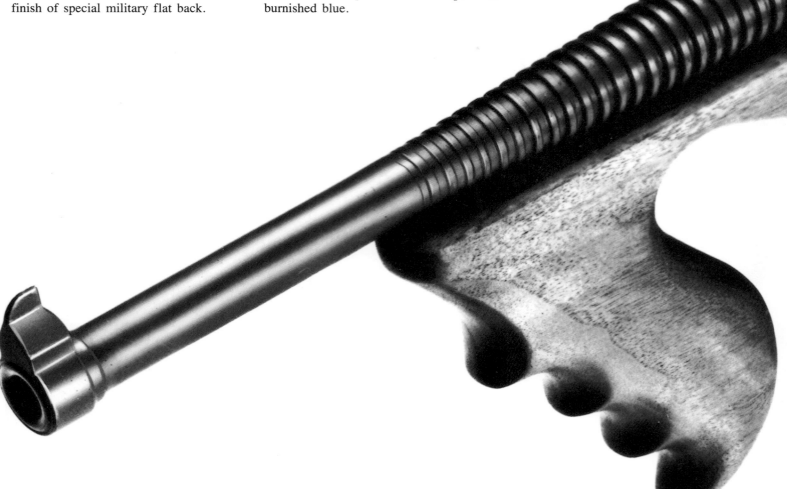

Above opposite: The Thompson 1927 A-1C Lightweight shaves 20 percent from the carbine's weight with no loss in performance or handling characteristics, has such Deluxe model features as traditional finger-grooved vertical foregrip, adjustable rear sight and compensator, blue-burnish finish and handsome walnut stock and grips. The Thompson A-1 *(left)* in automatic mode is shown *here* in an unusual configuration—without a muzzle blast compensator, which usually is needed to keep the .45 Tommygun's muzzle from 'climbing' when firing. This particular A-1 personalized with 'pistol' styling (no butt stock), and with the Thompson drum magazine—the new models of which hold 39 rounds; the vintage originals (hard to get these days) hold 50 rounds.

The M16A1 Automatic Rifle was standard US Armed Forces issue for years, but was replaced by the M16A2 automatic 3-shot burst/semi-automatic model *(above)* shown *below* in the handy Commando Carbine configuration (with 16″ barrel and folding stock) and *at bottom* as an 'H-Bar' (heavy barrel) AR-15 Sporter civilian model. *Far right:* A SAC trooper guards a USAF B-1B bomber with his M16A2 Commando Carbine, at Offutt AFB.

Colt Industries

Colt M16 Series Automatic and Semi-automatic Rifles and Carbines

Type: Automatic rifle and carbine
(M16A1 models); automatic/
semi-automatic rifle (M16A2 model)

Caliber: .223 Rem, 5.56mm NATO and
7.65mm NATO

Barrel Length: 16″ (M16A1 Carbine), 23″
(M16A1 and M16A2 Rifles)

Weight: 6.5 lbs (M16A1 Rifle), 7.5 lbs
(M16A2 Rifle)

Stocks: Nylon

Sights: Standard Military

The **M16** model line has engendered the
M16A1 Automatic Carbine, the **M16A1
Automatic Rifle** and the **M16A2 Auto-
matic/Semi-automatic Rifle,** which has replaced the M16A1 as the US Armed Forces
standard issue firearm. The M16A2, more
versatile than the M16A1, allows for 3-shot
automatic bursts and/or semi-automatic
operation.

The relatively rare M16A1 Automatic Carbine, with its collapsible stock, would make
a handy sporting arm for brushy areas, but
Colt Industries has the sporting situation well
in hand with their M16 civilian counterparts
series, the AR-15 semi-automatics.

Soldiers of the US 82nd Airborne Division *(below)* give their M16A1s a rest during a lull in the Grenada invasion of 1983. The M16A1 also saw action during the Beirut crisis—as witnessed to by this photograph *(right)* of US Marines standing guard amid the rubble of the US Embassy.

Below: This is the seldom heard-of carbine version of the M16A1, shown *here* with stock extended *(upper view)* and 'collapsed' *(lower view)*. *Below right:* The simplicity of design and construction which is at the heart of the M16A1 is demonstrated in this exploded view. Another M16 variation is this Colt M203 Carbine/40mm grenade launcher combination *(above)*. *Above right:* The M16A2 Commando Carbine sees a lot of US Military guard duty.

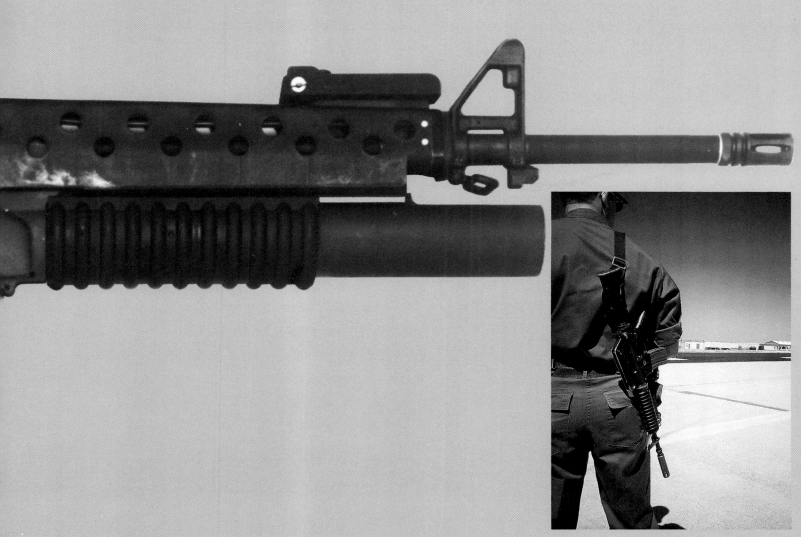

Above right: The Saco Defense, Inc M60E3 is a lighter weight variant of a US Armed Forces standby for the past 25 years, the M60 Machine Gun. The M60E3 features an ambidextrous safety, accurized sights and other improvements. M60 series machine guns have a 500-650rpm cyclic rate of fire. The SWD, Inc Cobray M-11 9mm Submachine Gun *(far right)* has a magazine capacity of 32 rounds, is 11.25″ long, fires at a rate of 900rpm and weighs just 3.75lbs.

Saco Defense, Inc

M60/M60E3 Machine Guns
Type: Gas operated, disintegrating link belt-fed, air-cooled
Caliber: 7.62mm NATO
Weight: 23.75 lbs (M60); 18.75 lbs (M60E3)
Length: 43.5" overall (M60); 42" overall (M60E3)
Magazine Capacity: Belt fed
Cyclic Rate of Fire: 500–650 rounds per minute

The **M60** has been in the U S armed forced inventory for over 25 years. It fires from an open bolt and features a quick change barrel with fixed headspace. The M60 is the basic model designed for dismounted infantry employment. Its variations include the lighter weight **M60E3** and other mounted (tank, helicopter) M60 configurations. The M60E3, as well as being lighter, features an ambidextrous safety, universal sling attachments, advanced sights, winter trigger guard, and foolproof charging.

SWD, Inc

Cobray M-11/9mm Submachine Gun
Type: Semi-automatic or fully automatic blowback
Caliber: 9mm Par
Barrel Length: 5.25"
Weight: 3.75 lbs
Length: 11.25"
Magazine Capacity: 32 rounds

SWD's **Cobray Submachine Gun** is compact, easy to fire, and steel constructed. Suited for police and tank, gun and mortar crew use, the magazine-fed gun fires from an open bolt and has an extended receiver to allow a slower rate of fire (approx 900 RPM). Available with an extendable stock that extends the overall gun length to 23", the Cobray also features a safety located to the right side and forward of the trigger guard.

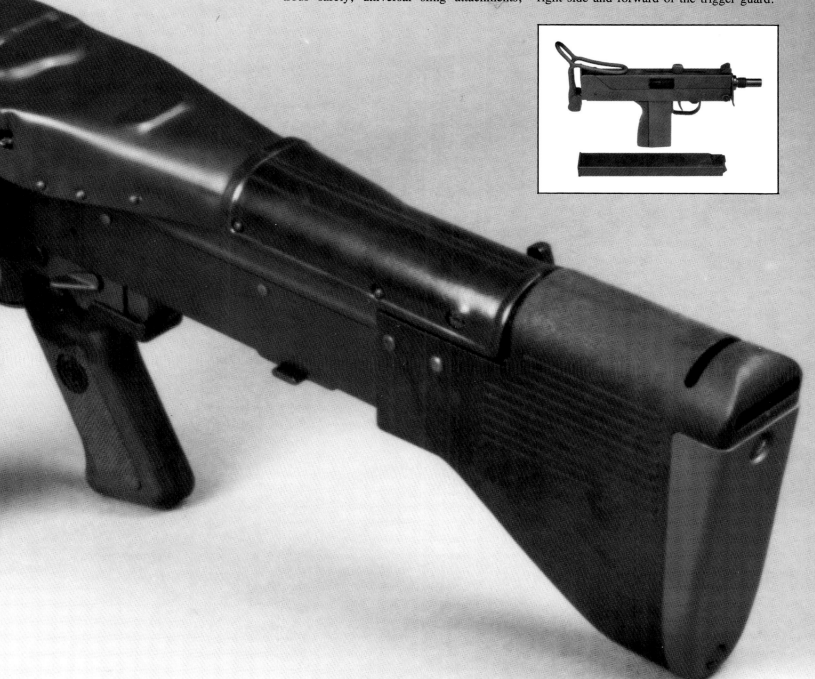

SHOTGUNS

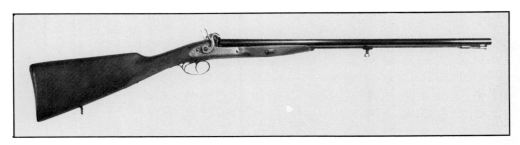

Hopkins & Allen Arms

Double Barrel Percussion Shotgun

Type: Muzzleloading long gun
Gauge: 12
Barrel Length: 28″
Weight: 6 lbs
Stock: Walnut

This Hopkins & Allen lightweight double features walnut stock with checkered wrist and forearm. The barrels are choked cylinder bore and hook breach designed for easy take down. The lock plates are engraved.

Ithaca Gun Company, Inc

Model 37 Featherlight Shotgun

Type: Pump action, single barrel
Gauge: 12 and 20
Barrel Length: 20″ to 30″
Weight: 5.75 lbs (20 gauge); 6.5 lbs (12 gauge)
Stock: Walnut
Magazine Capacity: 5 rounds

Originally introduced in 1938, Ithaca Gun's lightweight pump action now comes in 5 models, all featuring an exclusive bottom ejection that protects action from dirt and elements, receiver and action machined from high strength steel, rotoforged barrel, and raybar front sight. All 5 models are chambered for 2.75″ and 3″ shells and are available with various degrees of choke. The **Field Grade Vent** model with 3 tubes comes in 25″ and 28″ barrel lengths. The **Deluxe Vent** comes in barrel lengths of 26″, 28″ and 30″.

With a special bore choke, Ithaca Gun's **Deerslayer Featherlight** is available in barrel lengths of 20″ and 26″. A fourth **Supreme** model comes in barrel lengths of 30″ (12 gauge) and 26″ (both 12 and 20 gauge). The Featherlight fivesome is completed with a 12 gauge **Camo Vent** model that has a 26″ barrel, full choke and exclusive rust resistant 'Camo-seal.'

Model 37 Ultralite Shotgun

Type: Pump action, single barrel
Gauge: 12 and 20
Barrel Length: 25″
Stock: Walnut
Magazine Capacity: 5 rounds

Ultralite and **English Ultralite** shotguns with choke tubes are claimed to be the lightest pump action shotguns available. In-troduced in 1978, these guns have vent ribs and raybar sights, walnut stock and forend and are chambered for 2.75″ shells only. The English version is distinguished with its classic straight-grip stock and the standard Ultralite is also offered in a 20 gauge, 20″ barrel version with a special bore choke.

Model 37 Law Enforcement Shotgun

Type: Pump action
Gauge: 12
Barrel Length: 18.5″ and 20″
Finish: Parkerized and blue
Magazine Capacity: 5 or 8 rounds

The **Special LAPD Model** is Ithaca's most popular law enforcement model with a 18.5″ barrel. With varying degrees of choke, both

Above: The Hopkins & Allen Double Barrel Percussion Shotgun features hook breach design. Ithaca Gun Company's Model 37 Featherlight pump shotgun line includes *(below, descending)*: the Field Grade Vent; the Deluxe Vent; and the Model 37 Ultralight. USAF General Curtis LeMay *(right)* is an avid sports shooter.

Ithaca's LAPD model *(above)* has an 18.5" barrel, and is a popular law enforcement weapon. The DSPS II *(below)* and the M&P II *(bottom left)* both feature a 5-round magazine and a variety of chokes. Ithaca's Handgrip Shotgun *(bottom)* carries 5 rounds in its magazine and features maneuverability and 2 optional barrel lengths.

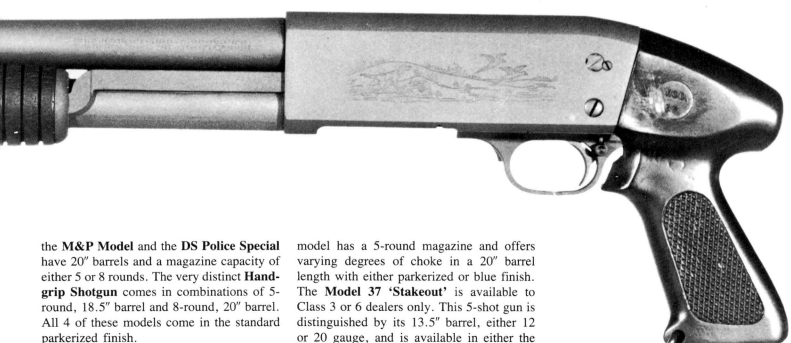

the **M&P Model** and the **DS Police Special** have 20" barrels and a magazine capacity of either 5 or 8 rounds. The very distinct **Handgrip Shotgun** comes in combinations of 5-round, 18.5" barrel and 8-round, 20" barrel. All 4 of these models come in the standard parkerized finish.

The **M&P II & DSPS II** law enforcement model has a 5-round magazine and offers varying degrees of choke in a 20" barrel length with either parkerized or blue finish. The **Model 37 'Stakeout'** is available to Class 3 or 6 dealers only. This 5-shot gun is distinguished by its 13.5" barrel, either 12 or 20 gauge, and is available in either the Parkerized or blue finish.

Ithaca Model 51A semi-automatics include the Deluxe Trap *(at top)* and the Turkey Gun *(mid-page)*, both of which are 12 gauge and carry 3 rounds. Ithaca Mag 10 semi-automatics are loaded with 3 rounds of 10 gauge knockdown power; in a bore favored by the legendary 'Shotgun Gibbs' of Wild West fame, Ithaca's design reduces recoil and delivers all the 10 gauge wallop to the business end. The Mag 10 Standard Vent *(above)*, the Standard Plain *(upper right)* and the Deerslayer *(lower right)* —equipped with adjustable rifle sights—are 3 of the Mag 10 models.

Model 51A Shotgun

Type: Gas-operated, semi-automatic
Gauge: 12 Mag
Barrel Length: 26″ and 30″
Magazine Capacity: 3 rounds
A Jim Tollinger design introduced in 1970, the **Model 51** was the first gas-operated semi-automatic to carry a lifetime operational warranty. The **Waterfowler** semi-automatic is available in a matte finish, 30″ barrel only. It features a full choke and sling and swivels. The **Turkey Gun** has the same characteristics of the Waterfowler but is offered in with the 26″ barrel only.

Camo Vent and **Supreme Trap-Skeet** models are available with both 26″ and 30″ barrel lengths. Sling and swivels accompany the Camo Vent model; the Supreme model offers a choice of full and skeet Ithaca chokes.

Ithaca Mag 10 Shotgun

Type: Gas operated, semi-automatic magnum
Gauge: 10
Barrel Length: 22″ to 32″
Magazine Capacity: 3 rounds
Noted for their minimal recoil and adaptability to steel shot, the **Ithaca Mag 10** line starts with the **Standard Plain**, 32″ barrel, full choke semi-automatic. The **Standard Vent** adds barrel lengths of 22″, 26″, and 28″

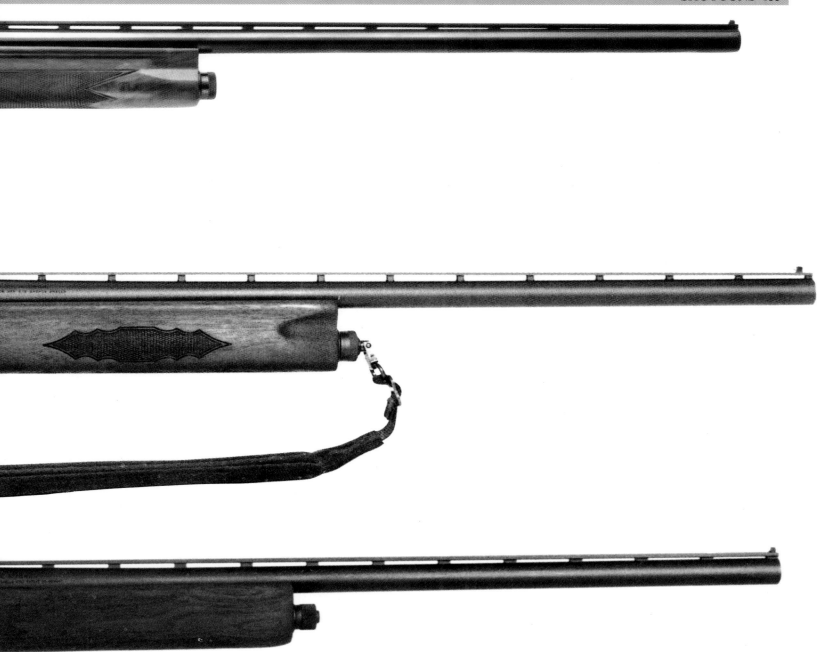

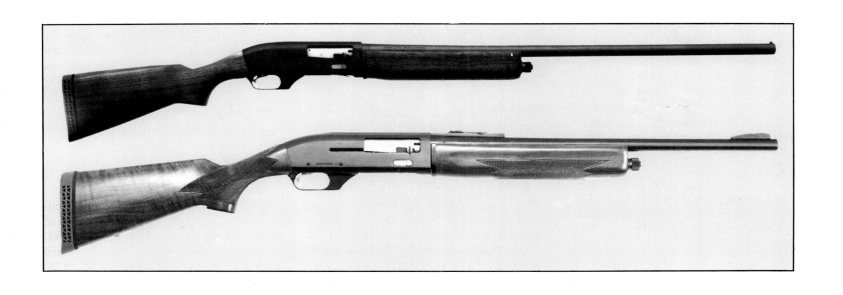

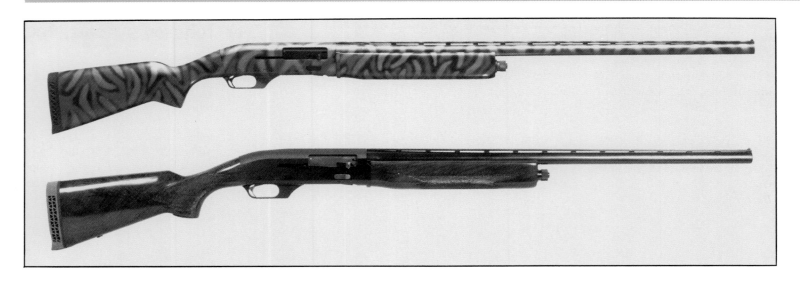

and the **Camo Vent** includes sling and swivels with 26″ and 32″ barrel lengths.

The **Deluxe Vent, Standard Vent with Tubes** and **Supreme** models complete the Mag 10 line. The Deluxe model is available in barrel lengths of 32″ and 26″ with full choke; the Standard Vent with Tubes has a 30″ barrel and the Supreme sports a 32″ barrel.

Mag 10 Roadblocker Shotgun
Gauge: 10
Barrel Length: 22″

Finish: Parkerized
Magazine Capacity: 3 rounds

Ithaca Single Barrel Trap Shotgun
Type: Pump action, single barrel
Gauge: 12
Barrel Length: 32″, 34″
Ithaca Gun's **Single Barrel Trap Shotguns** (**5E Grade** and **Dollar Grade**) are specially crafted collectors' items. Both models are 12 gauge with full chokes and available in barrel lengths of 32″ and 34″.

Iver Johnson's Arms, Inc

Champion Shotgun
Type: Single barrel
Gauge: 12
Stock: Walnut Finish
The Iver Johnson **Champion Shotgun** continues the Iver Johnson legacy of good workmanship for a fair price. Called the 'Farmer's Friend', this break action gun features positive lock auto-ejection, and is temporarily available with a full choke.

Upper left (above and below): The Mag 10 Camo Vent and the Mag 10 Deluxe Vent. *Above, middle and bottom:* The Mag 10 Supreme has a 32″ barrel; the Mag 10 Roadblocker has a 22″ barrel and holds 3 rounds; and the Ithaca 5E Grade Single Barrel Trap Shotgun is one of 2 specially crafted Ithaca collector's items, in 12 gauge, with full choke and barrel lengths of 32″ or 34″.

Ljutic Industries, Inc

Classic Ljutic Mono Gun

Type: Single barrel
Barrel Length: 34"
Weight: 8.63 lbs
Stock: Walnut

Built to individual specifications, the **Classic Ljutic Mono Gun** offers a pull or release trigger with removable guard containing the trigger and hammer mechanism. The firing operation consists of 8 parts, the receiver is of solid steel, and the rib—secured with 12 mechanical dovetailed rib posts—gives a 35.5" sighting plane.

Ljutic BiGun

Type: Single barrel
Barrel Length: 28" to 32"
Weight: 8.5 lbs
Stock: American and English walnut

Ljutic's ultimate in over-and-unders, the **BiGun** is available in **Trap, Skeet, International Trap,** and **Skeet and Live Bird** models. Barrel sets are interchangeable allowing the use of one BiGun for several styles of shooting. A second style offered is the **Ljutic BiGun Combo** which features an interchangeable top or bottom single barrel to accomodate trap, singles, handicap and doubles shooting. Single barrels are available with or without screw-in chokes and the Combo has a single speed trigger guard.

Ljutic Dyna Trap II

Type: Single barrel
Barrel Length: 33"
Weight: 8.5 lbs

The **Dyna Trap II** has the Ljutic pistol grip stock design and tapered forearm. Other features include the full choke barrel and a choice of Monte Carlo or straight back stock.

Ljutic Recoiless Space Gun With Rib

Type: Single barrel
Gauge: 12
Barrel Length: 30"
Weight: 8.5 lbs
Stock: Natural wood

Ljutic's in-line design gives a true perspective sighting plane for greater shooting accuracy and its lack of recoil promotes gun control. This shotgun features a screw-in choke barrel in choice of sizes, a pull trigger adjustable for weight and speed and release triggers with right or left handed actions.

LTD Over-and-Under Shotgun

Type: Single barrel
Barrel Length: 28" to 32"
Stock: English or American walnut

Ljutic's entry into the tournament competition TC series, the limited production over-and-under shotguns, feature a TC rib with accurate, quick pointing and tapered rib all incorporated together in unique rib line style. The exclusive double recess choke design produces centrally dense patterns with a short shot string.

Olympic Rib Mono Gun

Type: Single barrel
Barrel Length: 32"

With its choice of screw-in chokes or standard choke barrel, the **Olympic Rib Mono Gun** features a true mechanical sighting plane with the head held erect and the rib at eye level. Choke sizes range from .690 Super Full to .720 Improved Cylinder. Each gun is custom made to order. A second model, the **Modified Olympic Rib Mono Gun,** offers the same basic features with a rib height between the standard and the Olympic height.

Marlin Firearms Company

Marlin Model 55 Goose Gun

Type: Bolt action
Gauge: 12
Barrel Length: 36"
Weight: 8 lbs
Length: 56.75"
Stock: Walnut finished hardwood
Magazine Capacity: 2-shot clip

With its long, precision-honed full choke barrel, this Marlin **Model 55** is designed to bring down ducks and geese. The barrel, with its 3" Magnum shell capability, handles lead, steel shot, rifled slugs, and even buckshot. It has a thumb safety, red cocking indicator, brass bead front sight and U-groove rear sight.

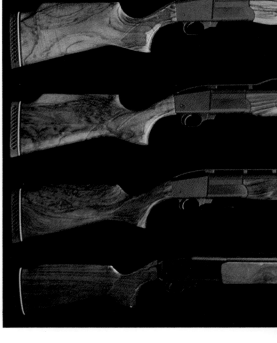

OF Mossberg & Sons, Inc

Mossberg Law Enforcement/Security Model 500

Type: Slide action
Gauge: 12 and 20, .410 bore
Barrel Length: 18.25" to 28"
Weight: 6.5 lbs average
Length: 39.75" overall with 20" barrel
Magazine Capacity: 6- to 9-rounds
  (Military Model 590)

Mossberg's **Model 500 Law Enforcement/ Security** series meets the stringent requirements of law enforcement weaponry. In a full range of barrel lengths, types, and fin-

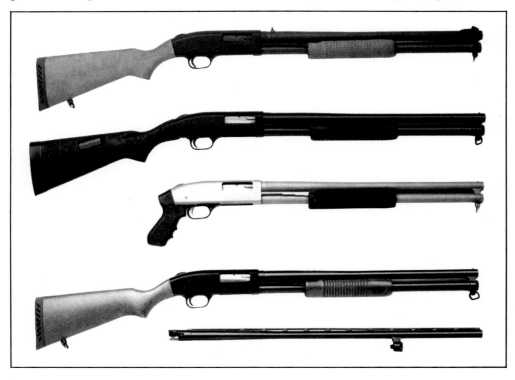

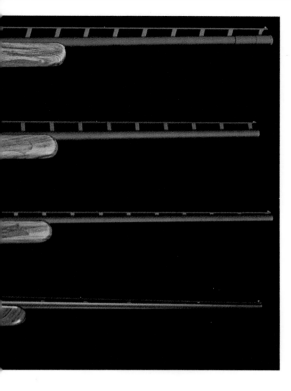

ishes, Model 500 shotguns possess a high-strength alloy receiver, disconnecting trigger, and an anti-jam elevator that remains up when a round is chambered. Other features are the machined steel bolt, positive shell extraction and ejection, and its overall proven endurance to fire 3000 consecutive rounds without malfunction.

Mossberg Law Enforcement/Security Model 3000

Type: Slide action
Gauge: 12
Barrel Length: 18" and 20"
Weight: 6.75 lbs
Length: 38.75" overall (18" barrel); 40.75" overall (20" barrel)
Stock: Synthetic
Magazine Capacity: 5-rounds
Mossberg's **Model 3000 Series for Law Enforcement/Security** are equipped with 1 of 3 synthetic stock styles. These guns have

an anti-jam feature which allows a chambered round to be fired, the action cycled clearing the jammed round and firing again. Receivers are machined from all steel, the bolt chromed or parkerized steel. Barrels chamber 2.75" and 3" rounds and the safety is a positive crossbolt with oversized button.

Mossberg Model 500 Shotgun

Type: Positive slide action
Gauge: 12 and 20, .410 bore
Barrel Length: 24" to 38"
Weight: 7.5 lbs (12 ga); 6.75 lbs (20 ga); 6.5 lbs (.410 bore)
Length: 48" overall with 28" barrel
Stock: American hardwood with walnut finish
Magazine Capacity: 6 rounds
The Mossberg **Model 500** is a slide-action shotgun built to stand up to the worst weather and tough hunting situations. The versatility of chokes and barrel lengths offered (down to an 18.5" barrel **Slugster** model) allows shooters to choose their own combinations. All models feature Mossberg's 'steel-to-steel' bolt and barrel extension, lightweight aluminum alloy receiver, double extractors for positive ejection, and a walnut finished stock with checkering and recoil pad.

Mossberg Model 712 Shotgun

Type: Gas-operated autoloader
Gauge: 12
Barrel Length: 24" to 30"
Weight: 7.5 lbs on 28" vent rib model
Length: 48" overall with 28" barrel
Stock: American hardwood with walnut finish
Magazine Capacity: 5 rounds
In a variety of barrel lengths and choke combinations, the Mossberg **712 Shotgun** is offered in Camo/Speedfeed and Standard variations including the **Accu II, Accu II Junior,** and **Slugster** models. Features include its solid 'steel-to-steel' lockup of bolt

and barrel extension, high-strength, lightweight alloy receiver, ambidextrous safety at top rear of receiver, dual shell latches, and self-adjusting action bars. In Accu II models the Accu-Choke II internal choke tubes sit flush with the muzzle and are unseen.

Mossberg Regal Series Shotgun

Type: Slide action (Regal 500) or autoloader (Regal 712)
Gauge: 12 (Models 500 and 712); 20 (Model 500 only)
Barrel Length: 24" to 28"
Stock: Walnut
Magazine Capacity: 5 rounds (Model 712); 6 rounds (Model 500)
The **Regal Series Shotgun** is identified by its cosmetic appeal. The walnut stock, contrasted with highly polished, blued metal parts, sports 18 line/inch cut checkering beneath the satin finish. The buttstock is accented by the pistol grip cap and contoured rubber recoil pad. The look is completed with a gold trigger and inlaid medallion on the receiver. Technical details include the safety which is located at the top rear of the receiver and Accu-Choke tubes, available to both models. All variations of the Regal Series can fire both 2.75" and 3" magnum loads.

Mossberg Model 1000 Shotgun

Type: Gas-operated autoloader
Gauge: 12 and 20
Barrel Length: 22" to 30"
Weight: 7.5 lbs (12 ga); 6.5 lbs (20 ga) with 28" barrel
Length: 48" overall with 28" barrel
Stock: American walnut
Magazine Capacity: 5 rounds
A gas-operated, low recoil autoloading shotgun, the Mossberg **Model 1000** is chambered for 2.75" shells. The series offers a variety of barrel lengths and chokes including the Multi-Choke II option in either gauge. All models feature an alloy receiver with scroll engraving, chromed steel bolt locks to steel barrel extension, internal gas metering system, crossbolt safety and firing pin block. Three competition models (**Trap, Skeet,** and **Super Skeet**) with barrel lengths of 25", 26", and 30" complete the 1000 series.

Ljutic Industries, Inc specializes in innovatively designed, highly personalizable shotguns. Shown at *top center* of this page are *(in descending order):* Ljutic's Olympic Mono Gun, the Modified Olympic Mono Gun, the Classic Ljutic Mono Gun and the Ljutic Dyna Trap II. *Far left, en bloc:* OF Mossberg & Sons, Inc's Law Enforcement/Security Model 500 shotguns feature 6-9 round capacity, an anti-jam mechanism and 3 bore sizes. The Mossberg Persuader *(bottom)* has optional short and long barrels. Mossberg's LE/SM Model 3000s *(left)* also have the anti-jam feature.

Mossberg Model 1000 Super Shotgun

Type: Gas-operated autoloader
Gauge: 12 and 20
Barrel Length: 22″ to 30″
Weight: 7.75 lbs (12 ga with 28″ barrel);
    6.75 lbs (20 ga with 28″ barrel)
Length: 48″ overall with 28″ barrel
Stock: Select American walnut
Magazine Capacity: 4 rounds

The **Select** series of **Mossberg 1000 Super Shotguns** distinguishes itself as the first autoloading series to shoot—within gauge—all 2.75″ and 3″ shells. There are no barrels to change nor levers or buttons to push. Both the 12 and 20 gauge versions deliver this performance because of their unique gas metering system which captures only enough gas to cycle the action. Mossberg has added looks to the Model 1000's performance capabilities: each receiver is machined from a block of steel, highly polished, then embellished with an elegant scroll engraving.

Mossberg Model 3000 Select Series

Type: Positive slide action with dual
    action bars
Gauge: 12 and 20
Barrel Length: 22″ to 30″
Weight: 7.75 lbs (12 ga with 28″ barrel);
    6.4 lbs (20 ga with 26″ barrel)
Length: 48.5″ overall with 28″ barrel
Stock: Select American walnut
Magazine Capacity: 5-rounds

A partnership of balance and weight, the Mossberg **Model 3000** series offers a solid grasp stock and forend with cut checkering, cold hammer forged steel barrel a receiver machined from a block of steel. All models handle 2.75″ and 3″ shells and possess double action bars, dual shell latches, a firing pin block and a mid-point bead on serrated vent rib.

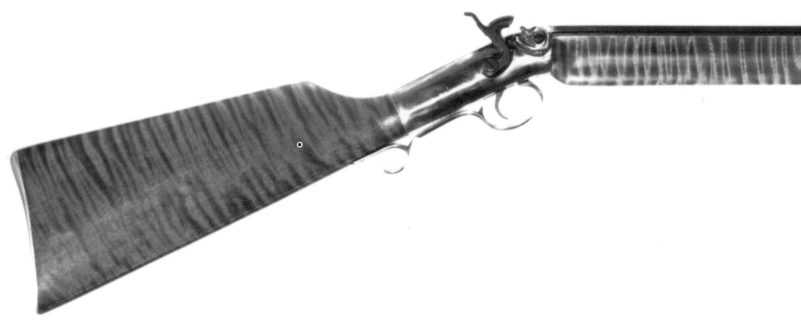

Mowrey Gun Works, Inc

Mowrey Muzzleloading Shotgun
Type: Box-lock muzzleloader
Gauge: 12 and 28
Barrel Length: 32″ and 36″ (12 ga) and 28″ (28 ga)
Weight: 7.5 lbs (12 ga); 6 lbs (28 ga)
Stock: Premium grade curly maple
The Mowrey **Muzzleloading Shotgun** is based on an Allen & Thurber design. Its box-lock action has two moving parts (trigger and tumbler) and both shotguns are available with either a brass or browned steel frame. The 12 gauge version features choices of a 32″ barrel cylinder bore, 36″ barrel cylinder bore, and a 32″ barrel with a screw-on full choke.

Navy Arms Company

Morse Muzzleloading Shotgun
Type: Single barrel muzzleloader
Gauge: 12
Barrel Length: 26″
Weight: 5.75 lbs
Length: 43″ overall
Stock: American walnut
Navy Arms' **Morse Muzzleloader** is a well-balanced American-made replica featuring a highly polished brass receiver and a bead front sight. The old Morse design has been modernized to make this an updated, good-looking weapon.

Remington Arms Company, Inc

Remington Model 870 Pump Action Shotguns
Type: Pump action
Gauge: 12 and 20

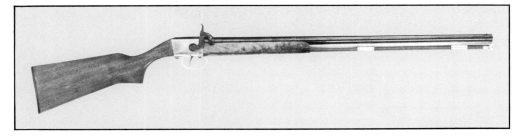

From the top down: Mossberg's Model 712 Accu II and 712 Slugster feature Mossberg's 'steel to steel' action; the Regal 712 and Regal 500 feature fine finish work; and the Model 1000 Super comes in 12 and 20 gauge, *shown here* respectively; Mowrey Gun Works, Inc's Muzzleloading Shotgun features fine craftsmanship and materials; and *(at right)* Navy Arms' Morse Muzzleloading Shotgun is a fine reprise.

Barrel Length: 20″ to 30″
Weight: 6 lbs to 7.25 lbs
Length: 40″ to 50.5″ overall
Stock: American walnut
Magazine Capacity: 5 rounds

Every **Model 870** repeating shotgun has a receiver machined from a solid block or ordnance-grade steel. Its action parts are 'vibrahoned' for smooth operation; the double action bars eliminate binding or twisting so that you get extra shots off as fast as you can pump and pull the trigger.

The **Standard Field Gun**, 'America's favorite pump shotgun,' has been in production since 1950 with over 4 million sold. This basic model has fast and smooth chambering and extraction through use of double action bars. Barrel interchanging is quick, no tools required. In addition to 12 and 20 gauge, special 28 gauge and .410 guns (the .410 has a 4-shot capacity) with butt plates are available.

With a variety of chokes including the 'Rem' choke and barrels measuring from 25″ to 30″,

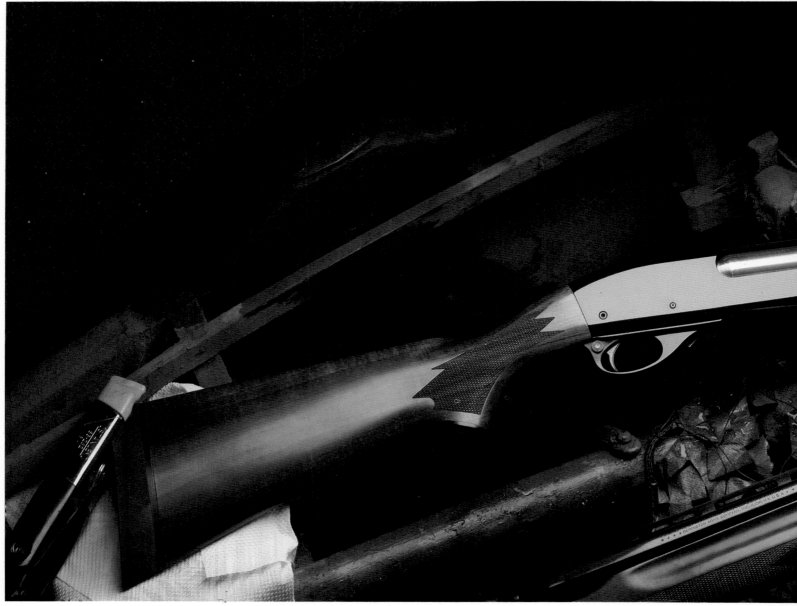

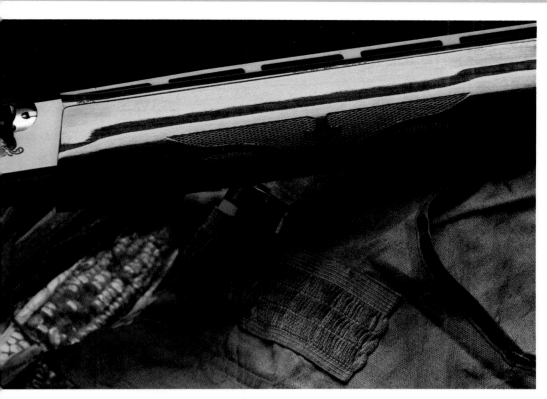

the **Field 870** has metal bead front sights. The **Wingmaster** model comes with ivory bead 'Bradley' type front sight and metal bead midsight. With special quickness, the **870 Special Field** model has a straight grip stock, shortened and slimmer forend and magazine, 21″ barrel and a 4-shot capacity. The **Brushmaster** with deluxe pump action has a shorter 20″ barrel and rifle sights—rear adjustable for windage and elevation. Designed primarily for hunting deer, it features an improved cylinder choke for maximum effectiveness with rifled slugs and buckshot loads. The lightweight 20 gauge **Youth** gun has a shorter stock and 21″ barrel; the **TA**

Below: Remington's Model 870 Pump Action Shotguns feature the famous 'Rem' interchangeable choke tubes, 'vibra-honed' parts for smooth operation, good looks and double action bars for quick repeating fire. Remington's Model 1100 automatics feature a recoil-reducing gas metering system, right- and left-handed versions, 7 styles and, as amply evidenced by the 1100 SA Skeet model *at left,* substantial-looking fine finish.

Trap Grade model, 12 gauge only, has an ivory bead front sight, white metal rear sight, special taraget grade sear, hammer and trigger assembly. The **Model 870 Police** (with sales restricted to law enforcement) is 12 gauge only with 18" and 20" barrels. **'Special Purpose' Magnum** and **Deer Guns** in the 870 series are 12 gauge shotguns custom designed for waterfowl and turkey and deer hunting. Barrels and receivers are Parkerized, and hard wood stocks and forends have a low lustre satin oil finish that protects against moisture. The **Magnum** comes in 26" barrel with Rem choke and 30" barrel with full choke. It also features 3" chambers for full magnum performance. The **SP Deer Gun** with 3" chambers has a 20" barrel and rifle sights.

Remington Model 1100 Autoloading Shotguns

Type: Gas-operated autoloaders
Gauge: 12 and 20
Barrel Length: 21" to 30"
Weight: 6.5 lbs to 7.75 lbs
Length: 39.5" (Youth Gun) to 50" overall
Stock: American walnut
Magazine Capacity: 5 rounds

With the Remington shotgun receiver machined from a solid block of steel as its base, the **1100** series adds a unique gas metering system that significantly reduces recoil, allowing a hunter to stay on target shot after shot. The **Remington 1100** is the

Above, descending: Durable, rugged and versatile, the Remington 870 series of automatics include the 870 Field Grade, the Wingmaster, the Special Field, the Brushmaster and the Youth Gun. *Below:* Model 870 receivers are milled from solid blocks of ordnance-grade steel. *From the top down, opposite page:* A Remington 1100 TA Trap model with Monte Carlo stock, a Model 870 Competition Trap gun, a left hand version of the 1100 SA Skeet model and a Model 870 Brushmaster Deer Gun with rifle sights.

only autoloader made in popular specifications for both right- and left-handed shooters and it is available in any of four gauges, seven styles, plus a host of interchangeable barrels. The 'Rem' choke with interchangeable choke tubes is available in 21″, 26″, and 28″ barrels.

For general hunting, the **Field Grade 1100** is the proven standard. The **1100 Magnum** takes over for versatility with hunting waterfowl. Both models come with a positive cross-bolt safety and metal bead front sights. The **1100 Special Field** model (with 4-shot capacity) combines a shorter overall length of 41″ with a lighter weight and English style straight line stock. The **Deer Gun** model is chambered in 2.75″ and has a 21″ barrel with rifle sights. Its improved cylinder choke delivers maximum effectiveness with rifled slugs and buckshot loads.

The lightweight **Youth Gun** model takes the same action and soft recoil and combines it with a shorter stock and barrel to reduce both overall size and weight. **SA Grade** and **Tournament Grade Skeet** models with skeet choke combine 25″ and 26″ barrels with 12, LT-20, 28, and .410 gauges. Also available are **TA Grade** and **Tournament Grade Trap** models with 30″ barrels and full chokes.

'Special Purpose' Magnum and **Deer Guns** in the 1100 series are 12 gauge—designed for hunting waterfowl, turkeys and deer, respectively. Both have parkerized barrels and receivers and hard wood stocks and forends with a low luster satin finish to protect against moisture. The **Magnum** has 3″ chrome-plated chambers and is available in barrel lengths of 26″ and 30″. The **SP Deer Gun** has a 21″ barrel fitted with rifle sights.

Remington 'Sportsman' 12 Autoloading Shotgun

Type: Autoloader
Gauge: 12
Barrel Length: 28″ and 30″
Weight: 7.75 lbs
Length: 48″ to 50″ overall
Stock: Walnut stained hardwood
Magazine Capacity: 5 rounds

The **'Sportsman' Autoloader** is available with three interchangeable choke tubes in a 28″ vent rib barrel or a 30″ full-choke barrel without choke tubes. This shotgun features the same proven reliability and low recoil sensation of Remington's gas operated autoloading system. The autoloader has a 2.75″ chamber.

Remington 'Sportsman' 12 Pump Shotgun

Type: Pump action
Gauge: 12
Barrel Length: 28″ and 30″
Weight: 7.5 lbs
Length: 48.5″ to 50.5″
Stock: Walnut stained hardwood
Magazine Capacity: 5 rounds

The popularly priced **'Sportsman' 12 Pump** features a 3″ chambered, 12 ga vent rib barrel in either 28″ Mod or 30″ full choke. Its receiver is machined from a solid block of ordnance steel. Featuring fast and smooth chambering and extraction through the use of double action bars, this shotgun has barrel extension locks in the breech bolt to assure constant headspace.

Savage Industries, Inc

Fox Model B Double Barrel Shotguns
Type: Side-by-side double barrel
Gauge: 12, 20 and .410 bore
Barrel Length: 24″ to 30″
Weight: 7 lbs
Length: 39.75″ to 45.75″ overall
Stock: Select walnut

In a variety of lightweight barrel/choke combinations, the **Fox** shotgun is a deluxe side-by-side double barrel shotgun featuring a walnut buttstock and semi-beavertail forend, cut checkering, ventilated rib, and automatic ejectors. **Model B-SE** has a single trigger, and **Model B** has a double trigger.

Stevens Model 311 Double Barrel Shotguns
Type: Break action hammerless, double barrel
Gauge: 12 and 20, .410 bore

Barrel Length: 24″ to 30″ (Model 311); 18.25″ Model 311-R
Weight: 6.25 lbs to 7 lbs
Length: 35.25″ (Model 311-R) to 45.75″ overall
Stock: Walnut finished hardwood

The **Stevens Model 311 Double Barrel Shotguns** from Savage Industries feature ventilated-rib and lightweight barrels, coil mainsprings, and double triggers. The **Standard Model 311** has a walnut finished hard-

Savage Industries, Inc produces the Stevens Model shotguns, in honor of the fine small arms firm which Savage bought in 1920. *From the top, this page:* The Stevens Model 311-R Double Barrel Shotgun with law enforcement 18.5″ barrel; the Stevens Model 67 Pump with top tang safety; the 67-VR with ventilated rib barrel; the 67 Slug with rifle sights; and the Savage Model 69-RXL law enforcement riot gun. *Opposite page, descending:* Sturm Ruger & Company, Inc's Red Label Over & Under Shotguns in 12 gauge and stainless steel; and in 20 gauge with blued finish; and a closeup of the Ruger over-and-under breech, opened to show locking lugs and ejectors.

wood stock and forend and 3″ chambering for 12, 20 gauges and .410 bore in a variety of barrel/choke combinations. The compact law enforcement **Model 311-R** has a hardwood stock finished with oil, rubber recoil pad and is available in 12 gauge only.

Stevens Series 67 Pump Action Shotguns

Type: Hammerless pump action
Gauge: 12, 20 and .410 bore
Barrel Length: 21″ to 30″
Weight: 6 lbs to 6.5 lbs
Length: 41″ to 49.5″ overall
Stock: Walnut finished hardwood
Magazine Capacity: 4 rounds

The **Model 67 Pump Action Shotgun** has a side ejection steel receiver and top tang safety. It is chambered for 3″ in 12 and 20 gauge and .410 bore. Barrel lengths range from 26″ to 30″ in varying gauge and choke combinations. The **Model 67-VR** is available in all the same variations with a ventilated-rib barrel.

The Stevens **Model 67-VRT** has the versatility of 3 guns in one with an interchangeable choke tub set. It's available in 12 and 20 gauge with a 28″ ventilated-rib barrel. A newer lightweight **Model 67 VTR-Y** was designed for a youth or small-framed shooter. This 6 lbs, 22″ barrel shotgun with a 12″ pull comes in 20 gauge only with 3 interchangeable choke tubes.

A rifled-slug version of this Savage firearm, the **Model 67 Slug** has a ramp front sight with folding leaf rear sight. It's available with a 21″ barrel in 12 gauge only. The compact law enforcement version of the 67 pump shotgun completes the line. The **Model 69-RXL** is a 12 gauge shotgun with an 18.25″ barrel, tung oil finished hardwood stock and forend, rubber recoil pad, and attached sling swivel loops.

Sturm Ruger & Company, Inc

Ruger 'Red Label' Over-and-Under Shotguns

Type: Over-and-under
Gauge: 12 (stainless steel) and 20
Barrel Length: 26″ and 28″
Weight: 7 to 7.5 lbs (stainless steel)
Length: 42.88″ to 45″ overall
Stock: American walnut

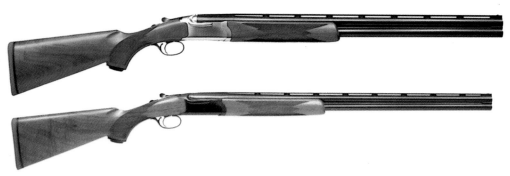

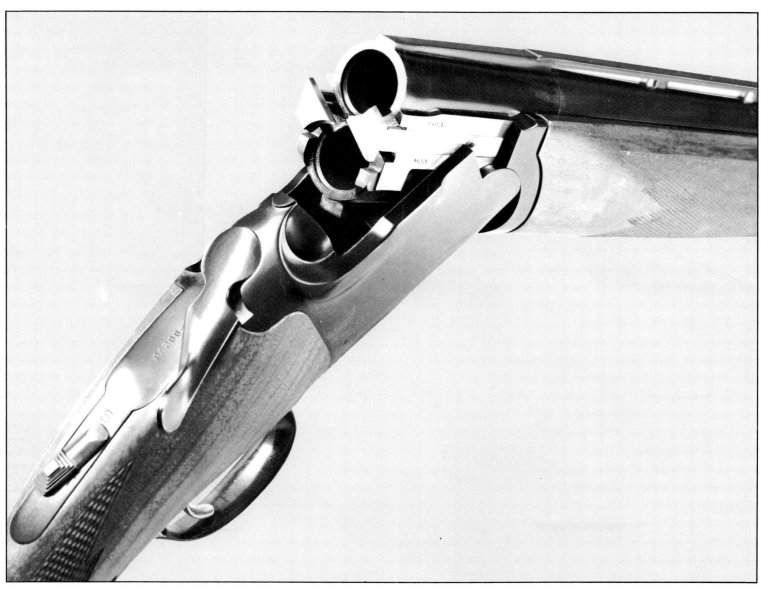

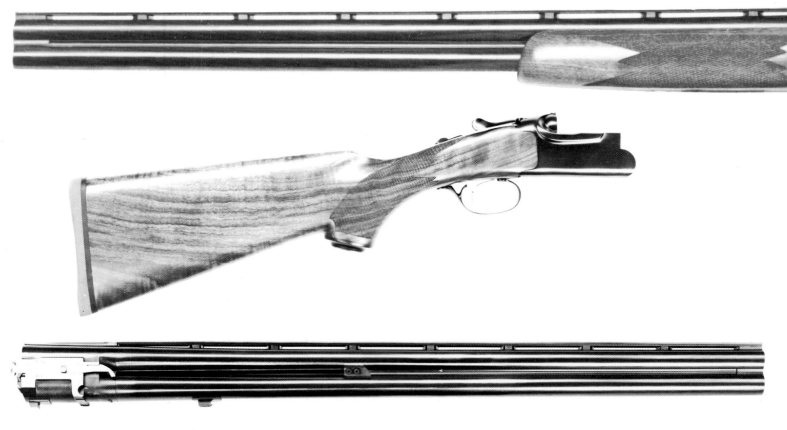

Sturm Ruger field grade **'Red Label' Over-and-Under Shotguns** are designed for strength and constructed of hardened chrome-moly and other alloy steels. Their unique patented hammer and trigger mechanism and single selective trigger provide several positive safety features. Available in a variety of chokes, all variations of the 'Red Label' Over-and-Under have a 14″ length of pull, 3″ chamber, and a gold bead front sight. The 12 gauge stainless steel models feature receivers, triggers, and forend irons made of stainless steel with a satin finish.

Thompson/Center Arms

New Englander Percussion Shotgun
Type: Single barrel muzzleloader
Gauge: 12
Barrel Length: 28″
Weight: 5.13 lbs
Stock: American black walnut
Thompson/Center's **New Englander** handles and points like a true bird gun. Equipped with a 28″ round barrel, it has blued steel furniture, color-cased coil spring lock and a hooked breech system that allows easy cleaning and the use of accessory rifle barrels.

US Repeating Arms Company

Winchester Model 1300 Shotguns
Type: Slide action
Gauge: 12 and 20 gauge
Barrel Length: 22″ to 30″

Weight: 6.25 lbs to 7.5 lbs
Length: 41.63″ to 50.63″ overall
Stock: American walnut
All versions of the Winchester **Model 1300 Shotgun** feature the 'Winchoke' system with interchangeable choke tubes and a specially adapted barrel. They also have dual action slide bars, a trigger-blocking cross-bolt safety and single pin takedown to permit easy field stripped. Model 1300 shotgun receivers are extruded from a high-strength corrosion-resistant alloy that reduces their overall weight and improves balance, handling and pointing. Barrels are rotary hot

formed steel and the front-locking rotary bolt with four locking lugs is machined from solid alloy steel.

The 12 gauge all-around **Model 1300 XTR Shotgun** has a 28″ ventilated: rib barrel, rubber recoil pad, and comes equipped with full, modified, and improved cylinder Winchokes and wrench. The **Model 1300 Featherweight Shotgun** is available in either 12 or 20 gauge, incorporates the Winchoke system with a 22″ ventilated-rib barrel, weighs in at 6.38 lbs and includes a recoil pad with the 12 gauge and a butt plate with the 20 gauge.

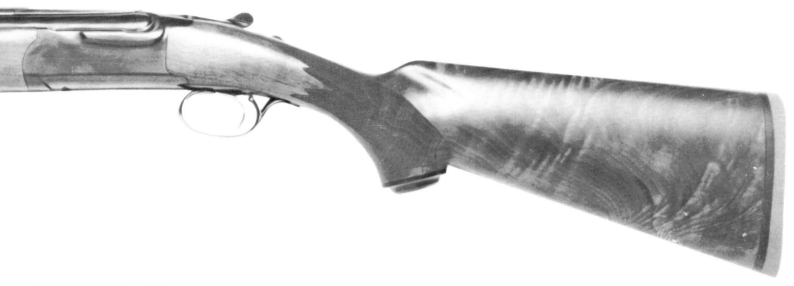

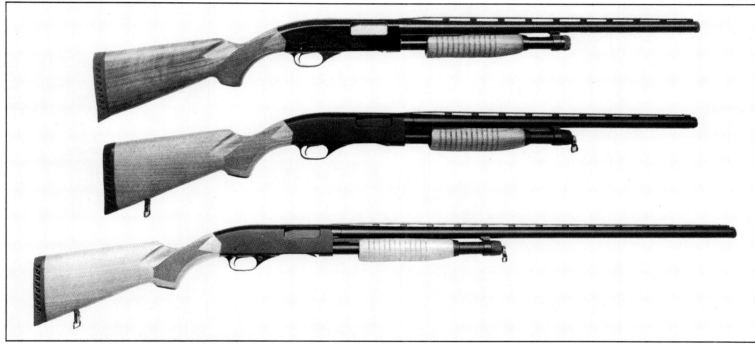

Winchester's **Model 1300 Turkey** is a 12 gauge shotgun designed for larger game fowl. It features a 22″ ventilated-rib barrel with the Winchoke system, non-reflecting finishes on the wood and metal, and comes with both a recoil pad and nylon sling/ swivels. The 12 gauge **Model 1300 Water-fowl**, designed for hunting ducks and geese,

combines all the same features with a 30″ ventilated rib barrel.

The Winchester **Ranger Slide Action Shotgun** comes in both 12 and 20 gauge with a ventilated rib, plain, or deer barrel. The **Ranger Deer Combination Set** in 12 or 20 gauge has two interchangeable barrels and rubber recoil pad. Its 24.13″ cylinder bore

deer barrel with rifle type sights handles standard and Magnum loads, rifled slugs and buckshot. Its 28″ ventilated-rib barrel features the Winchoke system. Lastly, the **Ranger Youth Slide Action Shotgun** is sized for smaller shooters in 20 gauge only. It has a repositioned grip and the option of a 22″ ventilated-rib barrel with Winchoke system or a plain barrel with a modified choke.

Winchester Ranger Semi-Automatic Shotguns

Type: Gas-operated, semi-automatic
Gauge: 12 and 20
Barrel Length: 24.13″ and 28″
Weight: 6.75 lbs and 7.25 lbs
Length: 44.75″ and 48.63″ overall
Stock: Walnut finished American hard-
    wood

Based on a proven record of service for over 20 years, Winchester **Ranger Semi-Automatic Shotguns** provide hunters with a range of versatility, features and styling.

Opposite, descending: The Ruger Red Label 20 gauge; and the Red Label 12 gauge, stripped to show its basic components. *This page, descending:* Some of US Repeating Arms' Winchester Model 1300 pumps: the Featherweight, the Turkey gun and the Magnum. *Immediately above:* The Thompson/Center Arms Percussion Shotgun can use accessory barrels.

Their self-compensating gas-operated action delivers repeat shots as quickly as the trigger can be pulled and the double positive cross-bolt safety is located conveniently at the front of the trigger guard. All Ranger shotguns are chambered for 2.75″ standard and Magnum shells interchangeably.

The **Standard Winchester Ranger Semi-Automatic Shotgun** is available in both 12 and 20 gauge with a 28″ ventilated-rib barrel, the Winchoke system, metal bead front sight, and cut checkered stock and forearm. This tried and true Winchester semi-automatic is backed by a two-year warranty.

The **Winchester Ranger Semi-Automatic Deer Gun** is available in 12 gauge only with a serrated butt plate, 24.13″ cylinder bore deer barrel with rifle type sights, and handles rifled slugs, buckshot, and all 2.75″ Magnum and standard loads. The versatile **Winchester Ranger Semi-Automatic Deer Combination** features the same 12 gauge with two barrels (deer and 28″ ventilated-rib) interchangeable on the same receiver. It has rifle-type front and rear sights.

Winchester Slide Action Security Shotguns

Type: Slide action
Gauge: 12
Barrel Length: 18″
Weight: 5.5 lbs to 7 lbs
Length: 28.63″ to 38.63″ overall
Stock: Walnut finished hardwood

Developed for police and security forces, these shotguns are chambered for 3″ shotshells. They have a recoil-assisted slide action that fires fast follow-up shots and twin slide bars to prevent binding in rapid fire. Other features include the one-pin receiver group disassembly, cross-bolt safety, rubber recoil pad and ribbed forearm for sure gripping and pumping and the 18″ plain barrel with cylinder bore choke.

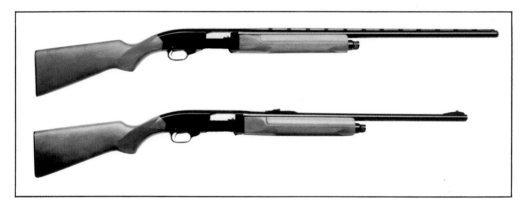

Available to the public are the **Defender** and **Marine Slide Action Security Shotguns**. The **Defender** model is a compact 38.63″ overall, has a five 2.75″ shell shotshell capacity and metal bead front sight only. A lightweight **'Pistol Grip' Defender** has a grip and forearm of impact-resistant plastic with a non-glare matte finish, shorter forearm ribbed for a positive grip, and a shorter 28.63″ overall length. The **Marine** model has an ordnance stainless steel barrel, chrome finish, shotshell capacity of seven 2.75″ shells, and rifle-type front and rear sights.

Specially designed for and available only to law enforcement is the **Stainless Police** model with an ordnance stainless barrel that accomodates gas launchers and handles corrosive launcher rounds.

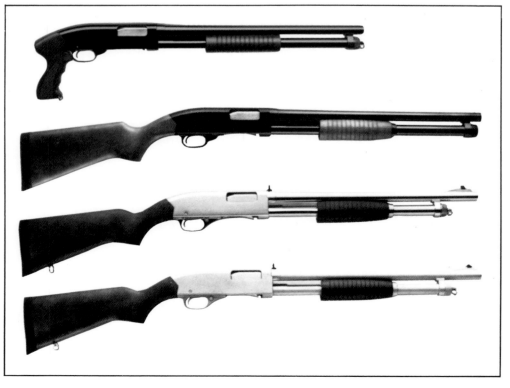

Left: The Winchester Defender slide action shotgun is designed for security and police work, with a recoil-assisted slide action, short overall length and 5 2.75″ shotshell capacity. *Opposite, top to bottom:* The Winchester Ranger Semi-Automatic Shotgun with a 28″ Winchoke barrel; the Ranger Semi-Automatic Deer Gun with rifle sights; the 28.63″ overall Pistol Grip Defender; the standard Defender with metal bead sight; the Stainless Marine model with rifle sights; and the ordnance steel barrel Stainless Police. US gunsmithing is alive and well—perhaps symbolic of its progress are these newer chapters from the Winchester story *(below, descending):* The Model 70 bolt action carbine; the Model 94 XTR lever action rifle and the Model 1300 slide action shotgun.

This soldier *(at right)* relies on his trusty partner, a Colt M-16, as he guards the huge Lockheed C-5A Galaxy *in the background*.

PART II:
THE MANUFACTURERS OF MODERN AMERICAN SMALL ARMS

COMPANY BACKGROUNDS

A-Square Co Inc
Route 4, Simmons Rd
Madison, IN 47250

A-Square was founded by its chief designer, Arthur Alphin—a firearms expert and instructor. In addition to having 700 days of field experience in Africa, Alphin holds a degree in weapons systems engineering from the US Military Academy, has served as a Lt Colonel in the US Army and lectures on military history and weapons systems technology as an assistant professor. Alphin's experience and training have led him to develop not only a line of powerful hunting rifles, but the ammunition and bullets which accompany them.

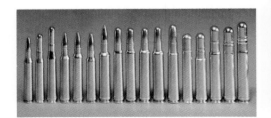

Arminex Limited
7882 East Gray Rd
Scottsdale, AZ 85260

In 1981 Arminex began its development of the Trifire by testing all existing semi-automatic pistols both in and out of production. Concluding that the 1911 pattern proved a superior firing system, Arminex set out to advance and update the basic 1911 design. Emphasis was placed on the marriage of a dependable single action firing system with an improved safety system. The resulting pistol with its firing pin lock in the slide is Arminex's solution for closing the gap between single action and double action pistols.

Auto-Ordnance Corp
West Hurley, NY 12491

The Thompson semi-automatic was the first weapon to be labelled a 'submachine gun.' Auto-Ordnance, founded by John Thompson, has changed hands several times over the years, but the 'Tommygun' remains one of the most recognized of American firearms and its patent remains one of their proudest possessions.

Auto-Ordnance revived the 1927 submachine gun series and modified them only to comply with current US firearms regulations. Many parts are made from the original tools and all trademarks are accurately reproduced.

TRADE MARK

REG. U.S. PAT. OFF.

Beretta USA
17601 Indian Head Hwy
Accokeek, MD 20607

Established in 1977 and manufacturing handguns since 1978, Beretta USA headquarters and manufacturing plant has united 450 years of Beretta expertise with US technology in this relatively new domestic program. All materials, components and labor pool for the Maryland facility are made in the US—with functions covering everything from engineering and production to finishing, assembly and quality control.

Browning
Route 1
Morgan, UT 84050

The gunmaker John Moses Browning was considered to be one of the world's most prolific gun inventors. During his 41 years of active gun design, Browning was granted a total of 128 patents involving over 80 separate firearms designs. Many of these inventions were sold to the great gun companies of the day and are recognized as among the most popular firearms of the late 19th century.

Today the Browning Company continues to market a wide variety of firearms that are almost exclusively manufactured in Europe. At this time the Buck Mark 22 Pistol is the sole Browning firearm to be produced in the United States (Salt Lake City), however, additional US production is planned.

Bushmaster Firearms
101 Hanover St
Portland, ME 04101

Touted in magazines such as *Combat Arms, Gun Annual, Combat Handguns* and *Survival Guide,* the Bushmaster Assault Rifle and **Steel Receiver Pistol** have received attention for their reliability and firepower. The rifle draws on the designs of the M-16 and AK-47. Both weapons utilize the newest developments in the field of weapons technology and the improved materials and tools currently available.

Champlin Firearms, Inc
PO Box 3191
Enid, OK 73702

Headed by George Caswell, Champlin Firearms offers a wide variety of options to anyone interested in purchasing a Champlin rifle. In operation for close to 20 years, Caswell not only produces and tailors the Basic Bolt Action Rifle but buys and sells many other one-of-a-kind firearms.

Chipmunk Manufacturing, Inc
114 East Jackson
Medford, OR 97501

Chipmunk Manufacturing produces a single shot sporting rifle suitable for use by 'the entire family.' In addition to the basic rifle, firearm production is limited to their Silhouette pistol. The balance of the Chipmunk line is devoted to related accessories including a scope mount base and a custom designed gun case.

Colt Industries
PO Box 1868
Hartford, CT 06101

As a boy, Samuel Colt had been interested in explosives and conducted numerous experiments with them. Legend has it that he conceived of a revolving cylinder weapon when he was a young seaman, the idea stem-

Opposite page, from left, top to bottom: A-Square Co Inc's founder Arthur Alphin and an A-Square Hannibal sporting rifle; some of A-Square's fine custom ammunition; various Auto-Ordnance decals and paraphernalia; Beretta's Maryland facility; a Browning custom rifle safe; Browning flexible gun cases; the Champlin Firearms logo; and Chipmunk Arms' rifle-packing chipmunk logo.

ming from the ship's wheel which could be stopped in almost any position by its clutch. In 1832 he submitted his first pistol and rifle for patenting.

Following the Texan-Mexican War and 1842 dissolution of the Patent Arms Manufacturing Company of Paterson, NJ, whose patents reverted to Colt's control, Samuel Colt began development of a .44 caliber pistol with a 9″ barrel which weighed over 4.5 lbs. Government orders were forthcoming for the .44 and other models including a .31 caliber pistol, a 'Wells Fargo' model, and several Dragoon pistols.

The demand for dependable repeating arms did not decrease and Colt filled orders for western settlers, the US military and foreign countries. Just prior to the Civil War two new military models were developed, .36 and .44 caliber guns that weighed just over 2.5 lbs apiece. Samuel Colt died during the Civil War, in 1862, but successors carried on his work—introducing the famous .45 caliber center-fire 'Peacemaker' revolver in 1871.

This six-shooter became known as the Colt 'Frontier Model' and is produced today as the very popular 'Single Action Army' revolver. Its reputation is based on the fact that the Peacemaker was the traditional arm of the Old West, protecting settlers from hostile Indians and wild animals. It is closely linked with some of the west's most colorful characters including Buffalo Bill, Wild Bill Hickock and Wyatt Earp. Even Calamity Jane is said to have dispensed what was known as 'Colt justice.'

Enacting their famous roles *(left)* as the Lone Ranger and Tonto, Clayton Moore and Jay Silverheels brandish their Colts. The Lone Ranger's metaphysically-inspired silver bullets and incognito guardianship of the unarmed and defenseless added medieval depth to the concept of 'Colt justice.' The Colt sesquicentennial logo is shown at the *top* of this page. *Above:* American troops and their M-16s during the Vietnam War. *Right:* A soldier of the US 82nd Airborne Division checks his M-16A1 after touching down during a training exercise in Europe.

In 1877 Colt introduced its line of double-action revolvers which could be cocked and fired by a single rearward movement of the trigger. The .45 caliber Army and Frontier Model with various barrel lengths was one of the first. Following this, automatic pistols produced by Colt under a John Browning patent eliminated the break between barrel and cylinder by firing the cartridge in the barrel. The Colt .45 cal automatic continues to be armed services standard issue.

Over 150 years after Colt's first patents, the Colt name remains a popular synonym for fine firearms.

Especially respected and feared by the Viet Cong during the Vietnam War were long Range Patrol units, such as the one *at left,* armed with Colt M-16s. *Below:* This soldier in a US Army war game uses a MILES (Multiple Integrated Laser Engagement System)-equipped M-16 to 'shoot' his enemies without harming them—quite an advance over squirt guns and ketchup. *Right:* US Army Reservists do a military waltz through a forest with M-16A2s at ready. The M-16A2 seems promising to uphold the M-16 military tradition.

Coonan Arms, Inc
830 Hampden Ave
St Paul, MN 55114

Dan Coonan introduced his original Coonan .357 Magnum autoloader in 1982. Following the basic design of the Colt Model 1911, Coonan's very powerful pistol with its continuous firing of factory, high velocity .357 Magnum ammunition has a barrel made of stainless and alloy steel that gives shooters thousand of rounds of shooting before washing out. The Coonan model quickly found its audience in government and law enforcement agencies, so much so that Coonan was not able to meet the civilian demand for his design until late in 1983.

Coonan has since gone on to update and improve his original design. The Coonan 'Model B' .357 Magnum became available in 1986. New developments incorporated into the Model B include: a linkless barrel to increase reliability and facilitate field stripping; resculptured, thinner walnut grips; one pin, slotted mainspring housing; grip lock configuration to eliminate hammer bite; interchangeable blade assembly sights.

Dan Wesson Arms
293 Main St
Monson, MA 01057

Dan Wesson Arms found its origins in 1968 under the name of DB Wesson Co, Inc and a partnership between founders Dan Wesson and Carl Lewis. The DB Wesson organization shipped its first gun, a .357 Magnum, in August of 1970. Production of .22s and .44s followed, with the first .22 being shipped

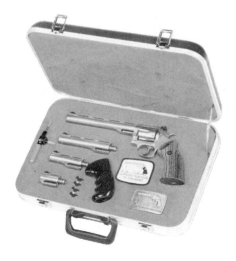

under the Wesson name in June 1979, the first .44 in January 1981.

In 1982 the company underwent the change to Dan Wesson Arms, headed by President Robert MacWilliams. Production has since expanded to include a variety of calibers from the current .22 to .375 Supermag revolvers. Because Dan Wesson Arms prides itself in the interchangeability of barrels and sights, there are few limitations to the Dan Wesson 'system.' You can keep any particular balance and trigger action and change barrels and shroud configurations at will.

Detonics Firearms Industries
13456 SE 27th Pl
Bellevue, WA 98005

'You get what you pay for' is the cornerstone of the Detonics philosophy. Detonics prides itself in its production of high quality, high powered, small and efficiently-sized pistols. Manufacturing combines the use of modern equipment with a high degree of handwork and pistolsmithing. Every gun is tested with a full clip of mixed ammunition before it is shipped to guarantee its safe, proper operation. To supplement their line of service and target pistols, the Detonics line is rounded out by its stainless steel extractor, .451 Magnum conversion kit and .451 Detonics Magnum cartridges.

Feather Enterprises
2300 Central Ave #K
Boulder, CO 80301

Feather Enterprises specializes in innovative, high-technology small caliber firearms, and accessories for same.

FIE (Firearms Import & Export Corp)
PO Box 4866
Hialeah, FL 33014

FIE both imports and exports guns from the United States. Manufactured domestically under the FIE name are .22s and .38 Specials. Imports range from .22s to 10 gauge shotguns and originate from countries as diverse as Italy, Germany and Brazil.

Freedom Arms
PO Box 1776
Freedom, WY 83120

Located in a mountain valley in Northwestern Wyoming, Freedom Arms produces a line of firearms that reflect their heritage from the Old West, when guns were perceived as everyday tools and not occasional recreation items. Designer and engineer Dick Casull oversees the development of all Freedom Arms weapons. A full line of accessories complements them.

Hopkins & Allen Arms
3 Ethel Ave
PO Box 217
Hawthorne, NJ 07507

With muzzleloading rifles and pistols in production since 1868, Hopkins & Allen has made a tradition of reproducing and refining this weapons art form. Their mainstay underhammer rifle production follows a design that is distinctly American (New England circa 1830). The action has only three moving parts and its clean lines, uninterrupted sighting plane and target trigger have long been recognized by black powder shooters. Many Hopkins & Allen muzzleloaders are available in kit form and certain models may be converted from percussion to flintlock and vice versa. Parts and accessories complete the full line of products.

In addition to their own United States manufacturing, Hopkins & Allen imports muzzleloaders from Italy.

Ithaca Gun Company, Inc
Terrace Hill
Ithaca, NY 14850

Founded in 1880 by Leroy H Smith who, with four brothers, manufactured both sporting arms and typewriters, the Ithaca Gun Company's first gun to be produced was a hammer model shotgun. Hammerless double-barrel shotguns were introduced in 1888, and single barrel traps in 1908.

Acquiring other smaller gun companies as it grew, Ithaca Gun produced and issued the world's first 10 gauge Magnum in 1932 and patented the hunting Model 37 Featherlight only 6 years later.

After decades of moderate growth and internal reorganization, Ithaca Gun introduced the Model 51 gas-operated semi-automatic shotgun in 1970. The Model 51 was the first shotgun of its kind to carry a lifetime operational warranty. The Mag 10, the first 10 gauge gas-operated semi-automatic Magnum, was in turn introduced in 1974.

With over 100 years of experience, the Ithaca Gun Company maintains that it has never lost sight of its 1885 pledge to endeavor to manufacture guns for the American sportsman that will 'meet the requirements of their own recognized standard of what a gun must be, and do, to suit the varied wants of so wide a range of shooting as this vast country affords.'

These pages, (top to bottom, left to right): The Dan Wesson Arms logo; DW System set and accessories; the Detonics logo and reloading kit; the FIE logo; the Freedom Arms logo, tilt-top pistol holster and .454 Casull Revolver; fine shotgun maker Lou Smith (1871-1957); and Al Ljutic with his Space Gun.

Iver Johnson's Arms, Inc
2202 Redmond Road
Jacksonville, AR 72076

Iver Johnson began his gunsmithing career in Bergen, Norway in 1857. By 1863 he had managed to scrape together the passage to Boston and, finding that the Civil War had produced a demand for gunsmiths in Worcester, he settled into a mechanics job at Allen & Wheelock.

Over the next eight years he added to his knowledge of guns, married and developed a working friendship with Martin Bye, a fellow immigrant and gunsmith. In 1871 Johnson and Bye began their own business. With the philosophy of 'a firearm for every bedroom and every cash drawer in the land,' they followed the formula of making the gun inexpensive, safe, compact, and above all . . . reliable. By the year of his death, 1895, Iver Johnson had built the largest handgun factory in the world and had earned the title of 'Armorer for the Nation's Bedrooms.'

Today, Iver Johnson's family carries on the tradition of their grandfather. As Luther M Otto III, the present administrator of Iver Johnson, said recently, 'We have worked 100 years so our customers can shoot in a split second'.

Jennings Firearms, Inc/Calwestco
4510 Carter Ct
Chino, CA 91710

Jennings Firearms is the exclusive distributor for the Calwestco-produced .22 LR pistol, the Model J-22. Parts, exclusive of the frame, are available and may be ordered separately. Repairs resulting from normal operation are made at no cost at the Chino, California plant.

Ljutic Industries, Inc
732 N 16th Ave Suite 22
PO Box 2117
Yakima, WA 98907

Founded by its president, Al Ljutic, Ljutic Industries produces high quality custom handmade firearms. The models are all patented and designed by Ljutic, who at age 18 began his shooting career and went on to win most of the nation's rifle championships from 1932 to 1940.

Still participating in rifle, pistol and shotgun shooting sports, Ljutic and his wife Nadine head this inventive Space Gun design and manufacturing company together.

The Marlin Firearms Co
100 Kenna Dr
North Haven, CT 06473

Born in Connecticut in 1836, John Mahlon Marlin worked at Colt's Hartford plant during the Civil War and in 1870 opened his own New Haven gun shop for business. So began what has become one of the industry's largest operations.

Marlin's philosophy was to manufacture better products even if it meant they were more expensive than those of the competition. From 1875 to 1890 Marlin produced Ballard single shot rifles and headed a team of designers who developed the Model 1881 repeating lever action rifle with .45/70 power. Other important developments under John Marlin were the side ejecting lever action rifle in 1889 and the Model 336 deer rifle design which was introduced in 1893. John Marlin died in 1901 and the firm was acquired in 1923 at an auction by a lawyer named Frank Kenna, Sr who became president of Marlin Firearms. The company has stayed in the Kenna family ever since. Moving the business a few miles away to North Haven, the Kennas have done much to update the century-old operation and have invested heavily in new machine tools and modern equipment. They cite the key to their success, however, in having maintained and restored the popular old styles while slowly introducing new ones. In fact, the two oldest models being manufactured today belong to Marlin: the Model 39 .22 lever action repeater (1891) and the Model 336 high power rifle (1893). Over two million 39s and over three million 336s have been sold to date.

Mitchell Arms
2101 East 4th St, Suite 201A
Santa Ana, CA 92705

Mitchell Arms specializes in unique, special performance weapons and accessories. All products have full product support with spare parts and warranty service available from the manufacturer. Special accessories made by Mitchell Arms include AK-47 Combat Knife-Scissors, swiveling and folding bipod and passive night sight.

OF Mossberg & Sons, Inc
7 Grasso Ave
North Haven, CT 06473

In business since 1919, OF Mossberg & Sons produces a wide range of shotguns and combination shooting systems that allow the purchaser to build a customized firearm to meet individualized specifications.

Mossberg also features a line of rifles and law enforcement shotguns, offering a weapon for most sporting and security situations.

Mowrey Gun Works, Inc
1313 Lawson St
Saginaw, TX 76179

Founded in the early 1960s, Mowrey Gun Works was one of the first companies to manufacture reproductions of 19th century muzzleloaders for commercial sale. Since its beginning the plant has been relocated, the equipment re-tooled, and some new designs incorporated into the line. In 1986 the company was taken over by general manager David A Higgins, Sr.

Again operating at full capacity, Mowrey Gun Works, Inc offers a wide distribution of its black powder guns and accessories. In production at Mowrey are a lightweight Squirrel Rifle, the Plains Rifle, 12 and 28

Two Apache scouts flank an Apache schoolboy in the pre-1884 photo *at left*. The scout *on the right* holds his '76 Winchester, and from the looks of his ammo belt, he's 'loaded for bear.' *Above right*: The Navy Arms logo. *Upper right*: The Remington Arms Company not only makes fine firearms, but also supplies shooters with a wide variety of ammunition. *Right*: Union troops charge Confederate barricades in a late Civil War battle. Both sides are using Springfields 'fixed' with the three-sided, barrel-collar bayonets of the time.

gauge shotguns and the recently added youth and women's black powder rifles. Mowrey Gun Works is also the exclusive producer of Ethan Allen-designed guns.

Navy Arms Company
689 Bergen Blvd
Ridgefield, NJ 07657

Val Forgett, the founder of Navy Arms Company, grew up with a fascination for muzzleloading firearms and Civil War history. This pastime eventually turned into his career, beginning with his service in the military as a technical advisor and firearms expert. In 1957 Forgett began to research the development and reproduction of original muzzleloading styles knowing that there would be a market in affordable and safe (to modern standards) replicas. His research took him to Europe where he made the decision to become an importer and distributor of sporting military weapons the world over. With its headquarters in Ridgefield and a plant acquired in 1970 in Union City, New Jersey, Navy Arms has added domestic production of firearms to their import business. The 1970s also brought to Navy Arms the acquisition of the black powder division of Ithaca Gun Company and Classic Arms of Palmer, Massachusetts.

North American Arms
1800 North 300 West
Spanish Fork, UT 84660

North American Arms has specialized in a three model line of 5-shot mini-revolvers designed for their uniqueness as a serious genre of firearms. The company also produces a line of accessories for its handguns.

Raven Arms
1300 Bixby Dr
Industry, CA 91745

Raven Arms produces a Model MP-25 pistol of all American-made parts in their California factory. In addition to completed pistols, most parts may be ordered direct from the factory. Frames, safety ball, plunger and spring are replaced at the factory only.

Remington Arms Company, Inc
Bridgeport, CT

Remington Arms had its beginnings when young Eliphalet Remington built his own flintlock at his father's forge near Utica, New York. Young Remington's rifle proved to be so accurate that neighboring sportsmen began ordering rifles from him. The year was 1816, and by 1818, the bulk of the business of his father's forge had been turned over to building Eliphalet Remington's sporting guns.

In this scene from the early days of railroading, it's evident that workers were wide open to Indian and bandit attack—that's why they stacked their arms military fashion in a central location—when they met each other at the rifle stack, they were reminded of who was on their side, and knew, more or less, where each other was—'which shadows to shoot at'—for considerable dust would be kicked up in the noise and confusion, and the black powder used then created, literally, clouds of smoke. The weapons shown *here* seem mostly to be Springfield breechloaders.

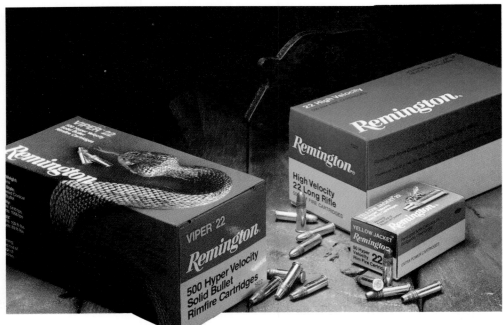

In 1828, Remington moved his business to a large factory he'd built near Ilion, New York. There, he and his son Philo began in earnest what was to be one of the largest and most well-respected firearm manufacturing businesses in the world. In addition to supplying the US Navy with its first breech-loading carbine, Eliphalet and Philo Remington pioneered such arms manufacturing techniques as the reflection method of straightening gun barrels and the gunstock

cutting lathe. Remington Arms produced the first successful cast-steel drilled rifle barrel in the US—enabling, with the stronger barrels this process produced, the eventual use of higher potency powder charges, creating greater ballistic flexibility and thus enhancing accuracy and knockdown power. This invention gave the US parity with any other arms-producing nation, and thus was of strategic importance. The federal government placed large orders for small arms with Remington at the start of the Civil War. Eliphalet Remington died on 12 August 1861.

The Remington Arms tradition of clean, smooth, classic lines and timeless designs continues, as does Remington innovation in the fields of firearms, ammunition and arms accessories. Remington Arms currently has six manufacturing plants and nine regional sales offices in the US, international offices located in the Federal Republic of Germany, Canada and Connecticut (a domestic international sales corporation). Remington continues to be an important contributor of small

arms to the US government, and remains a very popular supplier of sporting arms and arms accessories to sportsmen of many nations.

Saco Defense, Inc
291 North St
Saco, ME 04072

Saco Defense, a subsidiary of Maremont Corporation, entered the 1980s as the nation's primary producer of military machine guns, replacement weapon barrels from the 7.62mm to the 40mm bore sizes, and machine gun spare parts. The origins of the Saco division go all the way back to the period 1813–1826 when the Saco Manufacturing Company began to produce textile machinery and parts.

From the top down, left to right: Remington's interchangable 'Rem' Chokes give Remington Model 1100 and 870 shotguns added versatility; Remington's widely-known rimfire cartridges; Remington-Peters shot shells in an antique-style box; Rem Oil lubricant and rust protector; a .50 caliber M2HB (definitely not a 'small arm' and therefore not listed in this text) in the Saco test lab; and an infantry squad leader preparing to fire his Saco M60 light machine gun.

The Saco Defense M-60 machine gun has been US military infantry unit standard issue for over 25 years. Saco Defense began manufacturing military firearms during World War II.

Over 100 years later, the Saco Maine facility took on its first defense contract. It began to produce machine guns during World War II and, in 1959, Saco was selected to produce the M60 machine gun. Since that time almost one-quarter million M60s have been produced. In the period 1978–1981 Saco expanded production to include the M2HB machine gun. Current contracts cover many mounted machine gun models as well.

Savage Industries, Inc
Springdale Rd
Westfield, MA 01085

Its current ownership and title acquired as recently as 1981, the Savage name has been associated with firearms since 1895. In 1920 it acquired the assets and name of the J Stevens Arms & Tool Co.

Joshua Stevens founded the company bearing his name in 1864 to manufacture breech loading pistols and later rifles and shotguns. Instruments and tools for machinists were soon added to a complete line of firearms. The A H Fox Gun Co was acquired by Savage in 1930 and the name is still used today on Savage's top of the line double barrel shotguns.

Serrifile Inc
PO Box 508
Littlerock, CA 93543

Serrifile Inc began production of complete rifles in 1982, but, like many other companies they were caught in the insurance crunch and were unable to renew their liability insurance. In 1986, they ceased production of complete weapons. Fortunately, parts are still available for their Schuetzen rifles and the Terrier One Revolver.

C Sharps Arms Co Inc
PO Box 885
Big Timber, MT 59011

The C Sharps Arms Co charter is to provide the highest quality breech loading black

powder cartridge arms available. The original Sharps rifle, claimed to be one of the most powerful, accurate and respected guns in the 1870s, ceased to be manufactured in 1881. Recreated now, the Big Timber, Montana company is pleased to offer the New Model 1875, Models 1874 and 1863 and a wide variety of custom-made rifles.

Above left: The Saco Main facility. *Left:* The Savage Industries Indian head logo. C Sharps Arms has long been known for the long-range accuracy of their heavy caliber hunting rifles—hence, Sharps' 'The Scout & The Tenderfoot' logo *(above)*, with Sharps in evidence—the Tenderfoot having a rifle rest composed of two rods in an 'X'—de rigueur for the genteel shooter of the 1870s. Warm Springs Scout Donald McKay *(right)* poses with his Sharps in this 19th century photo.

Clockwise, from above: A Smith & Wesson Model 28 revolver is shown *here* being used as the control weapon in British pistol tests; a highway patrolman wears his Smith & Wesson Model 681; a Smith & Wesson Model 669 being 'drawn into action'; the Springfield Armory, Inc logo; a '1 of 10' Smith & Wesson custom model, featuring Smith & Wesson's fine engraving, available in 3 grades of coverage. This particular pistol celebrates the great state of Alaska's Silver Anniversary (1959-1984). Standard, machine or custom engraving is available for all Smith & Wesson pistols.

Smith & Wesson
2100 Roosevelt Ave
Springfield, MA 01102

Horace Smith and Daniel B Wesson began their first partnership in 1852 with the manufacturing of a lever action pistol that incorporated a tubular magazine and fired a fully self-contained cartridge. This repeating pistol was able to fire as rapidly as one could operate the lever which loaded the pistol and cocked the hammer, making it ready to be fired. The weapon, nicknamed the 'Volcanic' by *Scientific America,* was the team's first successful joint venture in firearms manufacturing.

The business that began in Norwich, Connecticut was eventually sold, the partners relocating to Springfield, Massachusetts in 1856 to design and produce a revolving pis-

tol which would fire a small .22 caliber cartridge. This new cartridge, eventually patented by the team in 1954, became one of the most famous cartridges ever developed. Originally called the 'Number One Cartridge,' it is more commonly known today as the .22 Rim Fire.

After the decline in business that followed the Civil War, Smith and Wesson sought to increase their market by displaying their arms at the 1867 Paris Exhibition. Due to the success of that exhibition and an increase in European sales, they introduced their 'Model Three,' their first large caliber (.44) revolv-

er. Its subsequent success throughout the world has helped the Smith & Wesson business to grow and prosper.

The success of the .44 was followed in 1880 with the introduction of a 'double action' revolver, and in 1899 Smith & Wesson developed one of its most famous revolvers, the .38 Military & Police. This revolver was designed to fire another first—.38 S&W Special ammunition.

The 1930s brought two more Smith & Wesson classics into the world: the K-22 Outdoorsman for the competitive shooter and the .357 Magnum for law enforcement. In 1949

the first American-made 9mm double-action pistol called the Model 39 was introduced, soon followed by the Model 29 .44 Magnum, for years the world's most powerful handgun.

Whereas its management has changed over the years, the Smith & Wesson name has thrived due to efforts to maintain development and production of guns that meet law enforcement and sportsmen's needs. A leader in the introduction of stainless steel for handgun construction, the Smith & Wesson operation has worked hard at and maintained its reputation as one of the world's leading handgun producers.

Springfield Armory, Inc
420 West Main St
Geneseo, IL 61254

Springfield Armory reserves the distinction as the United States' first official govern-

In this Frederick Remington painting, these cavalrymen wear new web belts—to carry .45-70 ammo for their newly issued Springfield carbines. Sidearms for these folks were probably Colts and a few old Remingtons—a mix of cartridge and cartridge-conversion (from cap and ball) revolvers.

FREDERIC REMINGTON

ment arsenal. So designated by an act of Congress in 1872, the company was originally founded in 1777 by George Washington who established it as a powder magazine and arsenal.

Starting with production of muzzle loading rifles as early as 1795, Springfield Armory grew from a federally operated supplier of military small arms to today's private enterprise manufacturer of gas operated semi-automatic rifles and high quality pistols.

Steel City Arms, Inc
PO Box 81926
Pittsburgh, PA 15217

Steel City Arms, Inc produces stainless steel autoloading pistols in calibers .22 LR, .25 ACP and 9mm Parabellum. Hand-assembled and designed as a back-up weapon for law enforcement officers, these pistols are also suited for more general protection purposes.

Left: The highly conjectural 19th century engraving *Heroic Death of Custer*—with Springfield carbines much in evidence. *Right:* World War I 'Yanks,' with grenade launchers fixed to their Springfield 30-06s. *Below:* A 19th century railroad construction crew, with pistols, axes and shotgun. *Overleaf:* This Johnson, Frye & Company engraving shows General Winfield Scott ordering the charge of McNeil's battalion at the Battle of Chippewa, during the War of 1812. Springfield was the chief armorer for the American forces.

Sturm, Ruger & Company, Inc
Lacey Place
Southport, CT 06490

The name Sturm in Sturm, Ruger & Company belonged to Alex Sturm who as a partner invested in the young business and was behind the design of the now-famous Ruger eagle emblem. The name Ruger belongs to Bill Ruger, the man who is behind every other facet of this 40 year-old firearms success story.

Bill Ruger grew up in New York state, fascinated with guns and engineering from an early age. As a student at the University of North Carolina, he gained attention and at least one job offer for his conversion of a Savage Model 99 lever gun to a gas-operated autoloader. In 1939 he designed his first machine gun and continued its development during the war years that followed.

It was in 1949, shortly following Sturm's untimely death, that Ruger was able to produce the first gun to bear the Sturm, Ruger Company name: the Autoloading .22 Pistol. The initial production of one thousand pieces were assembled, shipped, and sold—and the pistol has remained in production to this day. The 1950s brought the advent of the very popular Single-Six, Ruger Blackhawk and

S W D, Inc.

SWD, Inc
1872 Marietta Blvd, NW
Atlanta, GA 30318

In addition to manufacturing firearms, SWD also produces replacement parts, adaptors and a collection of accessories ranging from stock holsters to knives and shooters' bags.

Thompson/Center Arms
PO Box 2426
Rochester, NH 03867

The Thompson/Center partnership was formed in 1965 when toolmaker Kenneth Thompson and firearms designer Warren Center joined forces to manufacture the Contender pistol. Produced and sold in 1967, the Contender was the company's first product. Line expansion to include black powder firearms became a goal in 1970, and the first T/C Hawken rifle was produced and sold late that year.

As sales and production capacities increased, Thompson/Center added a new firearm to the line during each of the next few years including the Patriot Pistol in 1972, the Seneca Rifle in 1973, and the Renegade Rifle in 1974. They also began to make kit versions of many of the popular rifles available, adding on plant space as the business grew. Current production, distribution and admin-

.44 Carbine semi-automatic rifle in rapid succession. During the 1960s Ruger introduced the public to his No 1 Single Shot Rifle and the Model 77 Bolt Action Rifle. In the 70s Ruger introduced the Security-Six double action revolver to the police market, the 'Old Army' cap-and-ball revolver for blackpowder shooters, the Mini-14 in both military and civilian versions, and his first over-and-under 20 gauge shotgun.

Continuing on into the 1980s and throughout this relatively brief career, Bill Ruger has managed to introduce a new gun design on an average of one every one and a half years. The measure of his success must be viewed, however, not only in the quantity of designs, but in the continuing marketability of each of the models that have preceded them.

Top to bottom, left to right: Sturm Ruger & Company Inc's dramatic avian trademark; Ruger's Pine Tree investment castings plant; Bill Ruger; Ruger brassard, and double action pistol training school patch; the SWD, Inc logo; Warren Center; and Thompson/Center Arms' 1986 hunting logo.

istration of the complete Thompson/Center Arms line utilizes close to 170,000 square feet of operation space and 650 employees in Rochester.

Ultra Light Arms, Inc
PO Box 1270
214 Price St
Granville, WV 26534

Prompted by complaints of too-heavy hunting rifles, Ultra Light Arms set out to find ways to reduce overall weight without sacrificing accuracy or any other important features. In the early 1980s Ultra Light produced their first pair of lightweights and over the last several seasons they have been upgraded to today's three Series 20 models. All complete models are available with either right- or left-handed actions. In addition, customers may specify the stock's length of pull, color and finish.

US Repeating Arms Company
PO Box 30-300
275 Winchester Ave
New Haven, CT 06511

Celebrating a 120-year anniversary in 1986, the makers of **Winchester** firearms have an impressive record to recall. Originally founded in 1866 by Oliver F Winchester, US Repeating Arms today manufactures a variety of rifles, hunting shotguns, security shotguns and custom-made guns.

Weaver Arms, Ltd
PO Box 3316
115 N Market Pl
Escondido, CA 92025

Produced under the 'Nighthawk' trademarked name, Weaver Arms manufactures a single 9mm semi-automatic carbine. Field tested in 1983 and 1984 issues of *Gunworld*, *International Combat Arms* and other publications, the Nighthawk is accessorized with a carrying case, cleaning kit, magazine pouch and various items of wearing apparel.

Wilkinson Arms
Route 2, Box 2166
Parma, ID 83660

Wilkinson Arms manufactures two semi-automatic pistols, models 'Linda' and 'Sherry.' An extremely light and compact pistol, 'Sherry' is chambered for .22 LR in 4.38" overall. The 9mm Luger 'Linda' is designed and produced by John (Ray) Wilkinson who ensures that every Wilkinson Arms pistol is test-fired before leaving the plant.

Winchester
See **US Repeating Arms Company,** above.

This page, *top to bottom, left to right:* Thompson/Center Arms, Inc's Contender Pistol; T/C accessory case; T/C Numbers 8305, 8306 and 8307 Recoil Proof Handgun Scopes; T/C Patriot Pistol Kit; and T/C Frontier Rifle Cover.

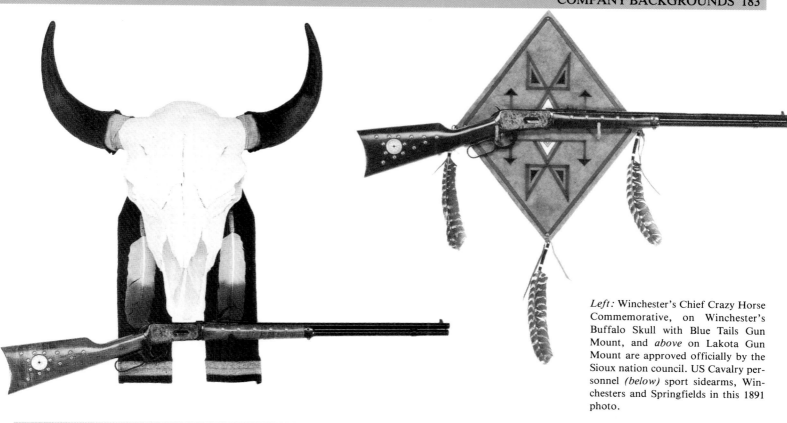

Left: Winchester's Chief Crazy Horse Commemorative, on Winchester's Buffalo Skull with Blue Tails Gun Mount, and *above* on Lakota Gun Mount are approved officially by the Sioux nation council. US Cavalry personnel *(below)* sport sidearms, Winchesters and Springfields in this 1891 photo.

Above: Though some claim that this famous duel at War Bonnet Creek was fought with knives, Charles Russell would have us believe that Buffalo Bill Cody *(left)* slew Yellow Hand *(right)* with a '76 Winchester.

APPENDIX:
TYPICAL ANNUAL PRODUCTION BY MAJOR US MANUFACTURERS

Pistols

	.22	.25	.32	.38	9 mm	.45	Total
American Derringer	16	12	4	217	362	1189	800
Arms Technology Ltd	9683	-	-	-	-	-	9683
Auto Ordnance Corp	-	-	-	-	3	908	911
Bellmore-Johnson Tool	-	-	-	3921	-	-	3921
Beretta USA	17,366	25,499					42,865
Chipmunk Manufacturing	478	-	-	-	-	-	478
Colt Industries	-	-	-	15,038	1026	39,302	55,366
Davis Industries	20,947	3499	3093	-	-	-	27,539
Detonics Manufacturing	-	-	-	70	3518	1044	4313
Dynamic Merchandising	-	-	2	-	-	-	2
Essex Arms Corp	-	-	-	-	-	1626	1626
Excam, Incorporated	1000	37,269	-	4881	-	-	43,150
Federal Ordnance	-	-	-	-	-	160	160
FIE Corp	2525	36,575	-	1216	-	-	40,316
Iver Johnson	19,377	339	230	2916	-	-	22,862
Jennings Firearms	69,751	-	-	-	-	-	69,751
Ranger Manufacturing	-	-	-	14,234	-	-	14,234
Raven Arms	-	133,700	-	-	-	-	133,700
Remington Arms	-	-	467	-	-	-	467
RG Industries	-	4937	-	-	-	-	4937
SWD	250	-	-	-	4251	2	4503
Smith & Wesson	5866	-	-	352	39,838	3512	49,568
Springfield Armory	-	-	-	-	-	41	41
Sturm, Ruger & Co	105,436	-	-	-	-	-	105,436
Thompson Center Arms	6012	40	2831	-	4289	2343	15,515

Revolvers

	.22	.32	.38 Sp	.357 Magnum	.44 Magnum	.45	Total
Colt Industries	5242	2380	9463	7986	896	468	29,949
FIE Co	18,300	-	5875	-	-	-	24,175
Freedom Arms, Inc	-	7884	-	-	-	1151	9035
Harrington & Richardson	20,306	14,894	-	-	-	-	35,200
North American Arms	18,927	-	-	-	-	168	19,095
Ranger Manufacturing	-	-	5371	-	-	-	5371
RG Industries	45,131	3090	28,433	-	-	-	76,654
Serrifle Inc	1123	3524	-	-	-	-	4647
Smith & Wesson	17,265	4117	186,214	176,127	76,326	5396	465,445
Sturm, Ruger & Co	9754	12,812	11,237	53,559	57,641	-	145,003

Law enforcement officers, no matter in what walk of life, tend to prefer Smith & Wesson revolvers (*note* the distinctive S&W handgrip protruding from the foremost officer's holster). The officers shown *here* guard the White House.